Happy Birthday!

Anna Hodson

12 August 1990

Shetland Ponies

SHETLAND PONIES

Anna Hodson

The Crowood Press

First published in 1990 by
The Crowood Press
Ramsbury, Marlborough
Wiltshire SN8 2HE

British Library Cataloguing in Publication Data

Hodson, Anna
    Shetland ponies.
    1.   Livestock. Shetland ponies
    I.   Title
    636.1'6

    ISBN 1-85223-288-9

Line-drawings by Claire Upsdale-Jones

Typeset by Acorn Bookwork, Salisbury, Wiltshire
Printed in Great Britain by Redwood Press Ltd, Melksham, Wilts

Contents

In memory of Max

Acknowledgements

Many people have helped me in the preparation of this book. Shetland breeders are as generous with their time and knowledge now as they were when I was setting up a stud in the 1970s, and I have had the pleasure of seeing again many people whom I knew in those days. I have also been generously welcomed by a number of Shetland people new to me. I thank them all.

I would like to thank everyone who made my visit to the Shetland Islands so enjoyable and so useful: first the Shetland Arts Trust for the grant that made it possible; then Helen Thomson, who laid on for me a programme of visits to all parts of the Islands; Tom Jamieson, who gave me many hours of his time; and Margaret Hunter, in whose company I spent a wonderful day on Unst. I saw many other people, too numerous to mention, while I was on the Islands, and I thank them all for taking the time to talk to me.

As for the photographs that illustrate the book, I am particularly grateful to the people who took photographs specially for me: foremost among these were Mrs Swinscow (Figs 116–24) and Mrs Toomer-Harlow (Figs 113–15), both of whom went to the trouble of re-enacting the breaking in of a pony. Others were Mrs Berry (Figs 96 and 100), Mrs Brooker (Figs 28, 60 and 61), Graham Hughes (Figs 105–10), Miss Minchin (Fig 9) and Mrs Osborne (Fig 65). Very many people responded to my request for the loan of photographs, and I am sorry not to be able to use one from each. I would like to thank the following: Mrs Adorian (Figs 75, 93, 97, 126 and 127), Mrs Braithwaite (Figs 64, 129 and 131), Dr Burgers (Fig 89), Mrs Carlisle (Fig 59), Mrs Carter (Fig 74), the Duchess of Devonshire (Figs 5, 27, 33, 36, 37, 104 and 130), Mrs Fox (Figs 66, 71 and 72), Mrs Hall (Fig 81), Lionel Hamilton-Renwick (Figs 2, 35 and 92), Mrs Hampton (Fig 53), Mrs House (Figs 38 and 47), Mrs Howell (Fig 30), Mr and Mrs Hughes (Figs 32, 91 and 99), Mr Tom Jamieson (Figs 80 and 86), Mrs Joyce (Fig 46), Mrs Kirkpatrick (Fig 42), Mr Lassen (Fig 90), Mrs O'Brien (Fig 31), Miss E. and Mr J. Smith (Figs 84 and 87), Mrs

Acknowledgements

Staveley (Figs 3, 39, 51, 57, 76, 112 and 125), Mrs Stevens (Figs 44, 55, 77 and 78), Mesdames Stevenson (Figs 40 and 103), Mrs Swannack (Figs 1, 26, 29 and 56), Mrs Swinscow (Figs 67, 68, 69, 70 and 73), Mrs Webb (Figs 49, 52 and 79), Mrs Whitaker (Figs 54 and 111) and the Woods family (Fig 58). The colour plate of Eastlands Sunstroke, Tibthorpe Peneleway and Five Squared of Crooklands was lent by Mrs Carlisle.

The Secretary of the Shetland Pony Stud-Book Society, Mrs Barbara McDonald, has kindly answered a number of queries.

A.H.
London, 1989

Introduction

*'The Shetland pony is the most lovable of
animals in the wide creation.'*

Thos Gifford

In the very first volume of the Shetland Pony Stud Book is a formal
description:

The Shetland pony is often very handsome, with a small head,
intelligent countenance, short neck, fine towards the throttle, back
short, quarters expanded, and powerful, legs flat and fine, and pretty
round feet; ribs well laid on until within two inches of the hip bone,

Fig 1   A beautiful Shetland: Hurtwood Sweet Biscuit, bred by
the late Miss Nan French and owned all his life by Mrs
Swannack.

9

having great width and depth near the heart and lungs, shoulders well sloped, fore-arm and thighs strong and muscular. The height of carefully-bred ponies from selected parents when full-grown will generally range from 9 to 10 hands.[1]

A fine creature indeed. The Shetland is the most distinguished of the native ponies. Everybody can recognise a Sheltie, not just by its small size, but by its especially attractive character. Thelwell struck a true note when he characterised the Shetland as 'the' pony. Yet no pure-bred pony can be so variable. A Shetland can be as tall as 42in (their height is always stated in inches, not hands and inches like other horses), or as small as 27in at maturity – a difference of 15in (or nearly 4 hands). Shetlands come in a greater variety of colours than any other breed: the classic blacks, glorious chestnuts and palominos, duns of every shade, greys, roans, bays, browns, and the eye-catching broken-coloured.

The Shetland pony's woolly winter coat is its greatest trademark: much needed in its native islands, where the winters are long and dark and stormy (with an average of 69 days of snow or sleet each year),[2] and still grown even in comfortable England – or in the

Fig 2   Small is beautiful: Fandango of Wetherden, 31in, meets an 18-hand Shire.

10

Fig 3   A pony in winter: Rustler of Markinch with snow on his nose. (Photo by Herbert Ballard.)

tropics. There is a thick undercoat and a hairy outer coat. The outer hairs can be 6in long or more, and they so muffle the outline of the pony that you can hardly see that it is a pony at all: 'Little shagged animals, more resembling wild bears than any thing of the horse tribe', is how Sir Walter Scott described them.[3] Yet in the summer, Shetland ponies are as sleek as racehorses. Sometimes it is hard to believe that the shining mares can be the mothers of the fluffballs-on-stilts that follow them.

Shetlands have another characteristic which is not so widely known but which forms a large part of their charm for the people who love them: their long life. It is not at all unusual for a Shetland to live to thirty years of age; even forty is no great age for them. Dr and Mrs Douglas, authors of the first book about Shetland ponies, make a touching comment: 'Everyone who really associates with them knows how disastrously short a time dogs and horses live: on no reasonable calculation can they grow old with their owners. Even the Shetland pony fails of this, but he makes the bravest of attempts.'[4]

No one should suppose that just because Shetland ponies are small and pretty they are simply toys. The late Major Maurice Cox, a great breeder and author of the standard work on Shetlands, was determined that: 'We must keep the breed as useful as possible and not a purely ornamental one.'[5] Their exceptional intelligence means that they can be trained to any job. A Shetland is the obvious choice for a child's first pony, not only because of its small size but also because of its superb temperament. Other advantages are its tough constitution and its uncanny sure-footedness; no child has ever taken a fall from a Shetland because it stumbled. As for driving, Shetlands have a brilliant natural talent for the work, being full of courage (which harness work demands, as the animal feels itself to be a long way from its human), and having extraordinary stamina. Mrs Christine Dick's famous pair, Peanuts and Pavlov, won thousands of fans for the breed with their exuberant performances

Fig 4   Mother's little helper: Seva Gaye Girl (owned by Mrs Hinde).

Fig 5   The last word: Braes of Greenock Valiant.

in the scurry at the Horse of the Year Show in the 1970s, but Shetlands had already been popular driving ponies among the cognoscenti for a century.

The special attraction of Shetland ponies has never been better described than by the Douglases:

> He provides . . . the dual charm of a creature at once wild and tame – wild in his strong instincts, his hardihood, and his independence – domestic in his wisdom and sweet temper, his friendly confidence in mankind, and his subtle powers of ingratiation.[6]

1

Origins of Shetland Ponies

EARLY EVOLUTION

The Shetland pony is not only one of the most distinguished of the many varieties of the horse but is also probably one of the oldest. Zoologists generally agree that the true horse (or pony) *Equus caballus*, originated in the plains of North America at the end of the Pliocene age (about 2 million years ago). A hugely successful species, it spread in all directions, and crossed over to Asia by the land bridge which then existed, where now the Bering Strait separates Alaska from Siberia. These early horses seem to have colonised the Old World in three waves of migration: the first went southwards and were eventually domesticated by the herdsmen of Mongolia and the early civilisations of China; the second – and the most important from our present point of view – went straight across the steppes of Asia and arrived in the forests and tundras of Europe; the last went south-west, across the mountains, into Iran, Arabia and North Africa.[1]

EUROPEAN PONIES

The early European breed of pony was a cobby type of about 12 or 13 hands high. The heavily wooded landscape of Europe in the aftermath of the last Ice Age did not favour a large animal. The temperatures, appreciably colder than at present, called for a well-developed protective coat. These characteristics can be seen in the prehistoric rock-paintings of Europe, which indicate that ponies were very numerous. Certainly they were hunted and eaten by Palaeolithic man; there is also a suggestion that ponies were tamed as long ago as 30,000 years.[2]

These cobby ponies were certainly very widespread, ranging right across Europe from Spain to Scandinavia. Confusingly, they are referred to in the zoological literature as 'Celtic' ponies; the ponies

15

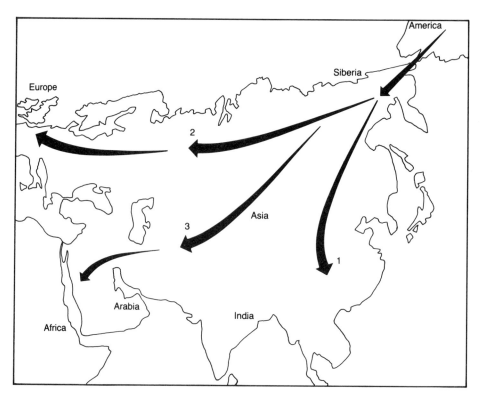

Fig 6 The migration of horses from America into Asia and
Europe.

themselves have no connection with the Celtic peoples or culture,
being far more ancient and widespread. These Celtic ponies were
certainly the ancestors of the Shetland pony, but they were much
larger. When and how did the Shetland become so small?

The Smallest Ponies

The science of genetics indicates that the process by which the Celtic
ponies evolved into the Shetland type was twofold. Firstly, there is
the tendency for animals that live in colder climates to be both
smaller and more compactly built than their relations elsewhere.
This arises from the overwhelming need to conserve body heat in
winter: heat generated by the metabolism inside the body will be
lost through the surface of the body, so it is best to have the
minimum ratio of surface area to body, i.e. to have shorter limbs, a
short back, thick neck, small ears, etc. This tendency (technically

desert fox

red fox

arctic fox

Fig 7   Allen's Rule: the extremities get smaller in animals that
live in colder climates. (After Ernst Mayr, *Evolution and the
Diversity of Life*.)

known as Allen's Rule), is seen in many animals (*see* Fig 7), and in
all northern races of ponies – Norwegian, Iceland, etc. – but at its
most pronounced in the Shetland.

Natural Selection

An even more important element is the fact that ponies living on
small islands have a restricted grazing range. When food is short, as
it is every winter on the Shetland Islands, animals that can get by
with little to eat are more likely to survive. Larger animals will tend
to die off leaving the smaller survivors to breed the following year. It
is important to realise that the smallness in populations of ponies
with restricted rations is not due to a direct stunting of the animals
through lack of food while they are growing, it happens through the
operation of natural selection favouring the genetically smaller
ponies and thus fixing the genes for smallness in the population. (In
the nineteenth century, before genetics became understood, breeders believed that if Shetland ponies were to be raised on good

grazing they would immediately become larger; there was some surprise when this turned out not to be the case.)[3]

It is also important to note that the pressure on Shetland ponies is not the harshness of the climate, but the rationing of food imposed by living on small islands; Norwegian and Icelandic ponies have to contend with equally hard winters but are able to find more food for themselves by grazing over wider ranges, and have therefore not been so severely selected for small size. However, there is a race of Norwegian ponies, living on the island of Bodo, which has become as small as the Shetland type, and for the same reason.[4]

To sum up, the first Shetland ponies were the typical Celtic ponies of Europe which spread north through Scandinavia and Britain (at the time when the North Sea was still land), and became more thickset through the operation of Allen's Rule. Then a small group of ponies became isolated on the Shetland Islands and, by natural selection, became smaller. There they were found by the earliest human settlers.

SHETLAND PONIES AND MAN

The earliest remains of ponies on the Shetland Islands are dated to about the sixth century BC, or about 2,500 years ago. The ponies' bones were found among the ruins of a late Bronze Age settlement at Jarlshof near Sumburgh, and they are of the same size as the Shetland ponies of today. It is not clear whether the Bronze Age farmers domesticated the ponies as they did the sheep and cattle. The ponies' bones are found scattered about, and it is a possibility that they were simply being hunted as prey, as were the seals and walruses whose bones were also found.[5]

The earliest evidence of ponies being used in the Shetlands comes from the time of the Viking invasion, in the early ninth century AD. The Vikings evidently brought their own ponies with them, for the archaeologists of the Jarlshof site note that 'the ponies were not of large size, but exceed the very small breeds on Shetland today'. It was also noticeable that the bones of the Vikings' ponies were nearly all those of adult animals. Very possibly they brought with them only strong ponies for war and work, and did not reckon on breeding in far-flung colonies such as Shetland; maybe they only brought males (the sex of the bones is not recorded, and is in any case not easy to distinguish).

Fig 8 The Bressay Stone. It is about a thousand years old and shows a pony that may be a Shetland.

The very fine sculptured stone known as the Bressay Stone, excavated near the remains of a very early church on the island of Bressay, opposite Lerwick, dates from about a century later. Its artistic style is a mixture of Norse, Celtic and Pictish, and its inscriptions in ogam lettering are undeciphered but for three words; it seems to show a priest or monk riding a pony (*see* Fig 8).[6] It is not possible to deduce what size of pony it was, given the artistic conventions of the time. This may be our first representation of a Shetland pony, or it may only be a Viking one.

THE SHETLAND TYPE – A PURE BREED?

The Shetland pony type has been remarkably resistant to outside influence given that it seems to have been already established by the time of the late Bronze Age. However, there is some variability within the breed, and some authorities (notably Major Cox and Dr and Mrs Douglas)[7] have stated that the small-headed, fine-boned ponies on Shetland are derived from the introduction, at some stage, of the 'Arabian' strain of horse (i.e. descendants of the third strand of migration mentioned on page 15). The great American zoologist George Gaylord Simpson has written that 'Domesticated local forms [of horse] were interbred from very early times, and it was not long before the types or (roughly) breeds established by man were such mixtures and recombinations of the original wild stocks that the idea of derivation of each main domestic type from a particular, natural wild population may be unrealistic or meaningless.'[8]

This seems to apply even to so remote a population as the ponies of the Shetland Islands. Both myth and historical records tell of various attempts to introduce new blood to the island ponies, and it is highly likely that the breed as it is now contains genetic contributions other than those that were present in prehistoric times. Any new blood that was successfully introduced into one herd could be expected to spread throughout the Islands, as there was (and is) significant interbreeding. Over the centuries this interbreeding has maintained the homogeneity of the breed. (This is in contrast to what happens when island populations are totally isolated from one another, as in the Galapagos Archipelago, in which case the races of animals and birds vary markedly from one island to another.)

Arab Horses

It is known that the horses used by the Roman army were bred by crossing European Celtic-type ponies with the taller faster horses of the Arabian type that the Romans had encountered in the eastern and southern parts of their empire. The resulting animals were 13 hands high or a bit over; their remains have been found in Britain, as far north as Hadrian's Wall. They could not themselves have come as far as the Shetland Islands, but it is a remote possibility that descendants of the Romans' horses spread among the native ponies of Scotland and went north, arriving eventually in Shetland.

The earliest feasible direct contact with horses of Arabian blood occurred in the twelfth century, when the Crusaders who went to Palestine encountered the impressive swift horses of the Saracens. Some of the knights brought eastern horses back home with them, and it is recorded in the Orkneyinga Saga that on Earl Rögnvald's return journey he went on horseback as far as Denmark, then by ship to Norway and then home.[9] It is possible that this knight and his companions brought the same horses with them all the way from the Holy Land to the Orkneys and Shetlands.

A myth persists that Spanish horses came ashore after the ship-wreck of the *Gran Grifon*, one of the flagships of the Spanish Armada, smashed on the rocks of Fair Isle in 1588. Even if the animals did manage to get onto the land (which would have been difficult on such a rocky coast and in stormy weather), it would not be at all likely that a Spanish horse would be able to survive the conditions on the islands. They were highly bred horses (their blood derived from the Arabian horses of the earlier Moorish rulers of Spain) and were admired throughout Europe for their speed and elegance, but they were not the sort to look after themselves out of doors. The possibility does remain, however, and one should not too hastily dismiss the stories that are found in popular mythology.

Norway

Throughout the Middle Ages Shetland's main contact was with Norway, under whose crown the islands remained until 1468 when they were pledged to James III of Scotland as part of the dowry of Margaret, Princess of Norway. There may well have been some importing of ponies from Norway to Shetland during these centuries, particularly if the Norsemen wanted to use larger ponies than those native to the islands, but the impact on the Shetland pony type would have been negligible as they were already drawn from the same ancestral stock as the Norwegian ponies. Before long the larger newcomers would have been weeded out by natural selection.

Iceland

Shetlanders have always believed that the white markings on piebalds and skewbalds derive from imported Icelandic ponies. (An alternative belief is that the origin is again Norwegian, but the Icelandic version is more usual.) Icelanders and Shetlanders have always been on neighbourly terms, and were both part of the Norwegian realm for a long time, so it is quite likely that ponies were taken from one place to the other. As for the white markings, they are caused by a single gene, and this gene could have arisen as a mutation among the native ponies at any time during their long history. It could have arisen independently in the Shetlands and

21

Fig 9   Skewbald ponies: Winchcombe Clare with foal (owned
and bred by Miss Minchin).

again on Iceland (certainly, its occurrence among the mustang
horses of North America is a separately-arisen mutation). However,
folk belief should again be given a fair hearing. It may be that the
mutation for white markings first occurred on Iceland and came to
the Shetland Islands as a deliberate import. Pied ponies may at that
time have been particularly admired (as they still are by gypsies and
many others) so that they were brought in as a prestigious rarity.
More recently they have been suspected of lack of stamina or poor
character, which ideas are without foundation.

More Recent Experiments

In 1837 a grey Arab stallion was run on the island of Fetlar (this
horse had an exotic history, having been a present from President
Simon Bolivar of Bolivia to Sir Arthur Nicolson, owner of the
island). The influence on the local ponies was said to have been
visible in the high proportion of grey ponies on Fetlar.[10] Later in the
nineteenth century another Arab stallion was brought in, and later
still a Highland pony stallion. At the time the Douglases were
writing (1912) there were two distinct breeds of ponies on Fetlar: the

true Shetlands and a larger type (11–13 hands) presumably derived from the Arab and Highland importations. Major Cox, writing half a century later, considered that the influence of these incomers on the Shetland stock of Fetlar was very slight, as there were many mares of true Shetland type on that island passed by inspection for the Stud Book.[11]

Unfortunate attempts to bring in larger ponies were recorded in the Statistical Account of the Shetland Islands in 1841:

> A pernicious practice has too much prevailed of crossing with larger and incongruous breeds from Scotland; and the progeny, as might have been expected, displays all the bad points, with few of the good, of the parents. A natural but rough antidote to these evils is, in some measure, to be found in bad seasons, which fall with fatal severity on the degenerate.[12]

The clear implication is that the attempts were, and deserved to be, unsuccessful, and did not have a lasting effect on the true Shetland type.

ONE TYPE OR TWO? – OR THREE?

No discussion of the history of the Shetland pony is complete without referring to the controversy among earlier writers as to whether there are two distinct types among pure-bred ponies, or indeed three types.

Major Cox pointed out that in all writings prior to the mid nineteenth century there is no mention of there being more than one type; he also remarked that the earlier writers were observant and knowledgeable about livestock, and could have been expected to mention the existence of two types if they had seen them.[13] There is no mention of different types in Volume 1 of the Stud Book, published in 1891. Yet by the turn of the century informed opinion was that there were, and always had been, two types. R.W.R. Mackenzie, founder of the celebrated Earlshall stud in Fife, seems to be speaking from experience:

> There seems no doubt that there always were on the islands two distinct types of ponies, one a thick dray-horse type, the other more bloodlike, which may be called the saddle type. Both have interming-

Fig 10   The 'Scandinavian' type: Thor.

led freely, and one finds even after careful mating an occasional reversion from one type to another.[14]

Dr and Mrs Douglas, whose book was the first monograph on Shetland ponies, wrote: 'The fact that the Shetland pony, as we have it today, is sometimes of a purely Scandinavian type, sometimes of an Oriental type, may perhaps be explained by regarding it as a composite of two distinct races.'[15]

Neither of these statements was made with the benefit of the knowledge of genetics that we have now; Mendel's work was not published in English until 1900, and it was many years after that before it filtered through to laymen. But in fact the Douglases have expressed in non-technical terms what a geneticist would expect to find: that the ponies are *sometimes* of one type, *sometimes* of the other. The implication is that the majority of ponies are somewhere in between. Further, the Douglases are doubtless right when they attribute these types to genes brought to the population by different ancestral stocks. The majority of ponies will carry a mixture of genes from each stock and will be 'middling', but sometimes the assortment of genes in a mating will produce a pony with a concentration

Fig 11   The 'Oriental' type: Marquis of Earlshall.

of one rather than the other. This is also what is referred to by Mackenzie when he finds 'occasional reversion from one type to another', and by the Douglases when they say elsewhere: 'Shetland ponies of this Oriental type do not form pure continuous or separate strains within the breed, but crop out here and there, sometimes the parents, and sometimes the progeny, of ponies apparently purely Scandinavian.'[16]

The Douglases go on to speculate whether the 'Oriental type' could be interbred so as to produce a race breeding true to type. A geneticist would say that the answer is almost certainly yes, but that it would take many generations, possibly as many as a hundred, to achieve it. As a generation of ponies is about three years (averaging out the maturing age of colts and fillies), this is an experiment that is not likely to be undertaken.

Miniature Ponies

It has also been suggested that there have always been three distinct types: the two mentioned above, and the miniature. This was the view expressed by Ian Sandison of Houlland, Unst, a very experienced breeder, in a personal communication to Major Cox.[17] Once again the true position is that although small ponies have been recorded for a long time (they were mentioned in the Statistical Account of 1841), they were not a separate type: they occurred as part of a continuum. Certainly, a pony under 34in is noticeably small, and would be likely to catch one's eye among a group of larger ponies, but it is also true that there are ponies of 35in, 36in and 37in commonly found so that there is no gap between the small type and the standard Shetland pony. However, modern breeders are making the attempt to set up separate strains of ponies under 34in high, and it is possible that they will eventually create a gap between miniatures and standard ponies. (This will be discussed further in Chapter 12.)

Photographs taken in the Shetland Islands in the late nineteenth century show every conceivable variation between the three types we have been discussing. It might not be totally unfair to say that one of the most common is a pony with heavy coarse head, upright shoulder, light bone and goose rump – not a sort that one would want to accept as one of the 'types' of the breed!

2

Historical Records

The Shetland Islands have always been surprisingly well populated for what seems such a bleak and unpromising place. Most of the communities are sited beside the sea, as the livelihood of the islanders has always depended to a great extent upon fishing. The crofters were fishermen, and the fishermen were crofters; or rather these tasks were the joint responsibilities of the members of each family. (Naturally all this has changed; the North Sea oil industry has brought modern employment to the Islands, and many people work in the tourist trade.)

Up until the 1840s, there were no roads at all on the Shetland Islands. Many journeys were made by boat, for nowhere in Shetland is much more than two miles from the sea (*see* Fig 12). But for journeys overland – perhaps to market or to church – ponies were used. If there was a load to be carried it would go on the pony while the owner walked alongside. A cart of any sort was out of the question because the route would lie along sheep tracks or untrodden heather and bogs. As for carrying people, a Shetland pony would carry a man of any size, even if his feet touched the ground on either side of it, or would carry man and wife both at once.

THE SEVENTEENTH CENTURY

The Shetland pony's power, stamina and surefootedness have been remarked on by nearly every literary visitor to the Islands. The earliest account is by Captain John Smith, who spent a year on the Islands in 1633: 'Their Horses, which they call Shelties, some of which I have seen, are little bigger than Asses, but very durable.'[1] At about the same time, Robert Monteith, an Orkney landowner, visited friends in Shetland and wrote about the ponies:

> The Horses are most of them of a very small Size, not exceeding nine hand-breadth high; an Horse of twelve hand-breadth hight (which is

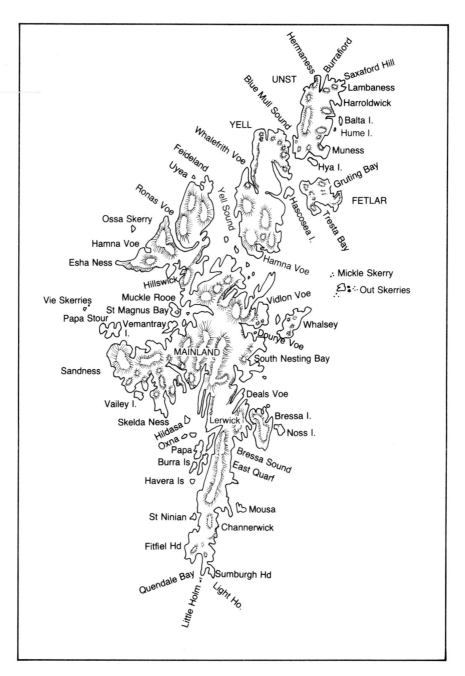

Fig 12   Map of the Shetland Islands as they were in 1856. No
roads are shown, as they were just then being constructed.
Many of the names are spelt differently now, e.g. Bressa on
the map for present-day Bressay.

but even rare here) is esteemed a very tall Horse, the least of the Horses here are sharp and full of Metle above belief, they will carrie a Man and a Woman twenty miles a day, and will live till they be 30 or 40 years old, though they never are put in a Stable Summer or Winter, and are not allowed Shoes or Provender, but shift for themselves in the open fields.[2]

A little later we find the first account of the Shetland ponies by someone who lived on the Islands. The Reverend Hugh Leigh was the minister at Brassie and Burns, and his description is rather like Monteith's: 'The Horses are of a little size and excellent Mettell: for one of them will easily carry a man or woman 20 miles a day; and they will live till they be 20 or 30 years of age though they never be stabled summer or winter.'[3]

THE EIGHTEENTH CENTURY

A fine description of Shetland ponies comes from John Brand, a minister sent to the Islands in 1700 by the General Assembly 'to visit and order the Churches there'. Whatever the impression he formed of the state of his brethren, he admired the ponies:

> I think the Kine and Sheep are of a greater Size than they are in *Orkney*, though their Horses be of a less: they have a sort of little Horses called *Shelties*, then which no other are to be had, if not brought hither from other places, they are of less Size than the *Orkney* Horses, for some will be but 9 others 10 nives or Handbreadths high, and they will be thought big Horses there if eleven, and although so small yet they are full of vigour and life, and some not so high as others often prove to be the strongest, yea there are some, whom, an able Man can lift up in his arms, yet will they carry him and a Woman behind him 8 miles forward and as many back: Summer or Winter they never come into an House, but run upon the mountains in some places in flocks, and if at any time in Winter the storm be so great, that they are straitened, for food, they will come down from the Hills, when the Ebb is in the sea, and eat the Sea-ware (as likewise do the Sheep), which Winter storme and scarcity of fodder puts them out of Case, and bringeth them so very low, that they recover not their strength till about St. John's Mass Day, the 24th. of June when they are at their best: They will live to a considerable age, as 26, 28, or 30 years, and they will be good riding Horses in 24 especially they'le be

the more vigorous and live the longer, if they be 4. Years old before they be put to Work. These of a black Colour are Judged the most durable, and the pyeds often prove not so good; they have been more numerous than they are now; the best of them are to be had in *Sanston* and *Eston*, also they are good in *Waes* and *Yell*, these of the least size are in the Northern Isles of *Yell* and *Unst*.

The Coldness of the Air, the Barrenness of the Mountains on which they feed, and their hard usage may occasion them to keep so little, for if bigger Horses be brought into the Countrey, their kind within a little time will degenerate; And indeed in the present case, we may see the Wisdome of Providence, for, their way being deep and Mossie in Many places, these lighter Horses come through, when the greater and heavier would sink down: and they leap over ditches very nimbly, yea up and down rugged Mossy braes or hillocks with heavy riders upon them, which I could not look upon but with Admiration, yea, I have seen them climb up braes upon their knees, when otherwise they could not get the height overcome.[4]

A slightly later witness, a Mr Campbell who lived five years in the Islands around 1750, also admired the ponies, but questioned whether they did any work:

There are little horses in the Island, which the Inhabitants call Shelties; they are so very small that one may lay his leg over them from the ground; but notwithstanding their Smallness they are both strong and active, and live many years, even until they are blind with Age: I have heard say, some of them live till they are upwards of thirty, and they are never kept within Doors, but are foaled in the Fields, live in the Fields, and die in the Fields. They do little work, unless it be to carry some Sea Weed, to dung the Ground in the Seed-Time. There is no Horse-hire.[5]

That is odd, because we have already read how much they were used as riding ponies. All levels of society rode them: there was no alternative. An English naval surgeon staying with a Shetland doctor in 1780 recorded that:

We were furnished with little horses and set out over hill and moor, rock and stone. We trotted along brinks of dreadful precipices where I would not venture to trust myself on the best hunter in England. The motions of these little Shetland horses are so very quick and short that I made many narrow escapes from falling over their necks.[6]

Describing the eighteenth century as 'the golden days of the Shetland gentry', a historian gives us a lively account of the role of the ponies in upper-class social life:

> They were all fond of active pursuits – were good sportsmen, oarsmen and horsemen – and were constantly on the move either for business or pleasure. Ponies and boats were frequently in requisition. In fine weather, even in winter, hills and dales were alive with these travellers – troops of gay gentlefolks on horseback, the steeds of the ladies often caparisoned like those of Spanish grandees, followed by retainers, barefooted or rivilined and wearing homespun, leading pack-horses with their equipments, and the gifts they brought each other.[7]

THE NINETEENTH CENTURY

Elaborate harness was evidently the fashion in the Shetland Islands. Here is Sir Walter Scott's description of a lady's mount:

> One of them . . . was decorated with a huge side-saddle of venerable antiquity – a mass, as it were, of cushion and padding, from which depended, on all sides, a housing of ancient tapestry, which, having been originally intended for a horse of ordinary size, covered up the diminutive palfrey over whom it was spread, from the ears to the tail, and from the shoulder to the fetlock, leaving nothing visible but its head, which looked fiercely out from these enfoldments, like the heraldric representation of a lion looking out of a bush.[8]

The journey to church was evidently a great occasion for ponies. Dr Hibbert, who went to the Islands several times in the 1820s, described the scenes:

> The peasant had returned home from the bleak scathold, where he had ensnared the unshod pony that was destined to convey him to the parish kirk. No curry-comb was applied to the animal's mane, which, left to nature's care, 'ruffled at speed and danc'd in every wind.' The nag was graced with a modern saddle and bridle, while on his neck was hung a hair-cord, several yards in length, well bundled up, from the extremity of which dangled a wooden short-pointed stake. The Shetlander then mounted his tiny courser, his heels scarcely spurning the ground. But among the goodly company journeying to the kirk, females and boys graced the back of the shelty

with much more effect than long-legged adults of the male sex, whose toes were often obliged to be suddenly raised for the purpose of escaping the contact of an accidental boulder that was strewed in the way. A bevy of fair ladies next made their appearance, seated in like manner on the dwarfish steeds of the country, who swept over the plain with admirable fleetness, and witch'd the world with noble horsemanship. The parishioners at length arrived near the kirk, when each rider in succession, whether of high or low degree, looked out for as green a site of ground as could be selected, and, without dismounting, carefully unravelled the tether which had been tied to the neck of the animal. The stake at the end of the cord was then fixed into the ground, and the steed appeared to be as satisfactorily provided for during the divine service as in any less aboriginal district of Britain, where it would be necessary to ride up to an inn, and to commit the care of the horse to some saucy lordling of the stables.[9]

Sir Walter Scott's romantic imagination was much excited by the Shetland Islands, which he visited in the 1820s, as he perceived them as much more primitive and free than Scotland at the time. He was under the impression that anyone could 'borrow' a pony and ride it:

> There is, indeed, a right of individual property in all these animals, which are branded or tattooed by each owner with his own peculiar mark; but when any passenger has occasional use for a poney, he never scruples to lay hold of the first which he can catch, puts on a halter, and, having rode him as far as he finds convenient, turns the animal loose to find his way back again as he best can – a matter in which the ponies are sufficiently sagacious.[10]

This may have been what actually happened, but it certainly was not sanctioned by law. Court records going back to the early seventeenth century tell of cases of men being fined for riding on stolen or 'grippit' ponies, the fines increasing for the distance that had been ridden.

Once roads were built on Shetland, in the 1840s, ponies were also used in harness. Whether or not this was an improvement can be guessed from a comment written some fifty years on, by an ornithologist visiting the Islands in 1895: 'At Voe the mails are changed over and I found that the 6½ miles between Voe and Brae must be walked as the mail-gig was a dilapidated old box affair with a small pony and string-fastened harness.'[11]

WORK ON THE CROFTS

Ponies were also used for farm work. Eliza Edmonston, a lady of one of the long-established families of Shetland gentry, wrote an excellent account of the Shetland Islands as they were in the 1850s, including a whole chapter on the ponies.[12] She says that 'every householder, high and low, has from two or three, to twelve and twenty brood mares'. Their duties (apart, of course, from breeding foals), were to carry out manure, and bring the hay, corn, or potatoes to the barn-yard. Miss Edmonston does not mention ploughing. Oxen were more often used for this, or it might be done by hand. Ponies did sometimes draw the plough, usually in teams, but it was thought to be very arduous for them. An account in the *Shetland Advertiser* of 1862 describes how it was usual to plough with a team of four ponies:

> They generally begin their labours at 6 o'clock in the morning and continue for two, three or four hours only, as the horses are soon exhausted. If they have another change of ponies they take them out to the field at 10 o'clock and plough to 12 o'clock. After dinner and at 1 o'clock they return to their labours out of doors and sow seed and harrow it, and remain thus occupied until 7 or 8 o'clock at night.[13]

FLITTING THE PEATS

By far the most important work that the ponies did was 'flitting' the peats. The only fuel available on the Islands (where there are virtually no trees, certainly none for firewood) was peat. It was dug (cast) by hand, in late May or June; a special spade called a tushkar was used, and the peat was cut into neat slabs and laid out in rows. That was men's work. Women's work was to turn the slabs to cure them, which took two or three weeks, with the rows being turned every few days. Then came the ponies to carry or flit the peat to the croft; this might be quite a distance away as the peat banks tended to be up in the hills (it is different from the bog peat of Ireland). Often mares would be used for this, with their foals running at foot.

The gear for the ponies consisted of a pad (flackie) of woven straw usually with a sack or some wool under it (*see* Fig 13). On this went a wooden pack-saddle called a klibber, with hinged sides held

Fig 13   The gear worn by ponies for flitting peats.

together by two wooden bars (nugs) which crossed at the top and projected so that the load could be hooked on to them. The klibber was held on by a belly-band (wime-girt) attached to a loop of rope at the bottom of each of the panels, and there would also be a crupper (tail-girt). The load of peat was put into a pair of baskets (keshies) made of plaited straw or rushes; one handle of the keshie was hooked on to the nug. To stop lumps of peat falling out, a net called a maishie was used; it was put on before the loaded keshie, being hooked over the nug on the opposite side so that it lay over the klibber when the keshie was put on and could be brought up and over the load and hooked on to the nug on the same side. The same gear was used for the various other loads that the ponies carried on the crofts – potatoes, hay, etc.[14]

Ponies were also used in the fish-curing industry, carrying barrels of salt outwards and barrels of cured fish back to Lerwick for export.[15] They also contributed to the fishing by supplying hairs from their tails for lines.[16]

Fig 14   Two klibbers. The one with two pairs of nugs
is the more usual type. (These are from the collection of the Walls
Museum.)

WINTER HARDSHIPS

Many of the travellers who saw the Shetland ponies in the Islands
felt moved to comment on the hardships that they endured, never
being brought in during the winter or being given fodder in hard
weather. Thomas Gifford, who was the leading landowner on the
Islands in the eighteenth century, was sorry for the ponies but
understood why they were treated so:

> It will no doubt be wondered at by strangers that so little care is taken
> about these sheep and horses, which are so useful and beneficial; the
> reason whereof is, that the poor inhabitants, having used their
> utmost endeavours, can scarce find food and shelter for their oxen
> and cows, without which they could not live; and in hard winters

many of them die for want of fodder, so that they have none to bestow on their sheep and horses until they find more time to improve the land.[17]

A more encouraging picture was painted by Miss Edmonston, who told how the ponies seemed to be able to foretell the hardest weather.

Indeed their instincts are so much more prompt and unerring than man's sagacity, or 'weather wisdom', that we unhesitatingly calculate on this very circumstance, that the *horses*, old and young, come to their owners' home-stead, or are found standing outside the wicket that leads to the common, immediately before a fall of snow. They are at once admitted, and fed with hay, – if there is any provided, – if not, with dried moor-grass or oat-straw. At the gentlemen's houses there may thus be seen as many as forty; indeed, then, and only then, may the owner see all his stock together at a time. If a foal be weakly, or a colt changing its teeth, it will probably be brought into the kitchen, where the children feed it with oat-cake and sweet-milk, and thus it becomes tame and familiar; so much so, that we have frequently seen the little creatures, if permitted, trot in and out of the parlour rather noisily, to be sure, but with perfect decorum.[18]

But this is an upper-class view, and one cannot suppose that the crofters' ponies could have expected the same kind of treatment.

3

Shetlands in Victorian Times – From the Parks to the Pits

There have always been three things that the Shetland islanders could sell – fish, Fair Isle knitting and ponies. The ponies must have been exported here and there for centuries, going to Norway or Holland or North Germany with the fishermen returning home after their trips to Shetland. This was not an organised trade, and did not deplete the stock of ponies remaining on the Islands, as the numbers involved were very small. During the eighteenth century more ponies were sold abroad, particularly to Scotland and England where they had become fashionable. The Douglases quote a letter sent in 1737 to a breeder on Bressay from Mellerstain, the seat of Lord Binning (heir of the Earl of Haddington) in the Scottish border country: the pony would not, after all, be required as Lady Binning's children had gone away to school and would be grown up by the time they returned.[1] Eliza Edmonston, who was very proud of the Shetland pony's high standing with the English nobility, knew of one pony 'so diminutive as thirty inches when full grown, and then it could be carried in a person's arms, and became a welcome though singular guest in an English drawing-room!'[2]

Sometimes Shetland ponies were used as decorative park animals; they were a change from the usual fallow deer, and easier to fence in. One such herd was the Marquis of Bristol's, at Ickworth, Suffolk. Records of his ponies, all black, go as far back as 1815.[3] More usually Shetlands were harness ponies, and they were considered extremely smart. The Marchioness of Salisbury was one of the most distinguished ladies of her time, and set the tone for elegant society even when she was in her eighties; she went everywhere in a low phaeton drawn by four black Shetland ponies, with postillions and outriders.[4] This was in the 1830s.

Fig 15   A Victorian basket phaeton.

Shetlands were not just fashionable, they were economical too: not just in the amount of food they required but in running expenses. Among the many taxes imposed to raise funds for the Napoleonic Wars were taxes on working horses and ponies and on carriages. These were on a sliding scale, with large horses and heavy carriages being charged most, and very small ponies and their vehicles being exempt altogether.[5] A gentleman might justify indulging his wife in a pair of Shetland ponies and a phaeton by reflecting that there would be no duty to pay.

THE EXPORT TRADE

At this time over a hundred ponies a year were leaving the Islands. In 1809 about 150 altogether were exported. In 1824 and 1825 the Parish of Tingwall alone exported 92 and 140 respectively.[6] There were perhaps ten thousand ponies on the Islands, so the numbers leaving were still negligible. By the middle of the century, however, the exports increased immensely. There were several factors involved. One was improved transport within Britain; up till then ponies had been transported 'on the hoof' along poor roads (the ponies that went to Ickworth travelled by ship to Hull and then some 120 miles to their new home along what were no better than cart-tracks).[7] With the building of railways, canals, and macadamised roads transport and therefore trade became much easier.

Another factor was America. Since gaining its independence from Britain at the end of the eighteenth century, the new country had become immensely prosperous. The Americans wanted to have – and could afford to pay for – everything that was best about the genteel British way of life, and high on their list was British horseflesh of all shapes and sizes. This of course included Shetland ponies. Large numbers of ponies crossed the Atlantic.

A CHILD'S MOUNT

By the middle of the nineteenth century, the prestige of Shetland ponies stood extremely high. More and more children were learning to ride (sons and daughters of newly rich manufacturers and merchants, as well as little lords and ladies), and the Shetland was considered the ideal mount. Sir Walter Gilbey, one of the most knowledgeable horsemen ever, was a keen supporter of Shetlands:

> The docility and good temper of the Shetland pony make him, above all, the best and must trustworthy mount for a child. Captain H. Hayes has remarked that 'a comparatively high degree of mental (*i.e.*, reasoning) power is not desirable in a horse, because it is apt to make him impatient of control by man.' The Shetland pony is the rule-proving exception; for he combines with the highest order of equine intelligence a disposition curiously free from vice or trickiness.[8]

Sir Walter had a famous Shetland pony of his own, called Good Friday, who won a number of first prizes in the 1890s. In Fig 16 he is being ridden by a very small boy in a basket saddle. Another picture of him, with his stable-mate a Shire, shows him to have been about 38in or 39in high; he is very definitely the riding type, with a well-laid-back shoulder and small head carried high.

Some children started riding even younger than this. There was a fashion for loading babies into panniers, baskets mounted on each side of a pack saddle. The infants either faced forwards or sat back to back, and if one was much heavier than the other, weights were used for balance. Donkeys were considered safest for this work, but ponies were classier, and Shetlands were best of all because mother

Fig 16   Good Friday.

or nurse did not have to lift the babies so far; miniature Shetlands were popular as pannier ponies.[9]

Frank Townend Barton, another of the great nineteenth-century horsemen, was equally sure about the suitability of the breed as a first mount: 'There is no better variety of pony for a child than a Shetlander', but he did not start the riders off so young. With a surprising streak of feminism he wrote:

> By the time that a child reaches ten years or thereabout it ought to be able to control a well-mannered Shetland pony whilst in the saddle, and the sooner a child is taught to look after herself (or himself) a little, the better horseman it will become.[10]

Then look at them!

> The Park is alive with little mobs of boys and girls galloping, trotting, and walking as little as possible . . . How bright they look, how happy

40

Fig 17   A family ride.

with innocent excitement glowing on their rosy faces! . . . And then what pluck the little creatures have; and how bravely they imitate their seniors, in handling ponies a little bigger than Southdown rams![11]

The family ride in Fig 17 is evidently taking place in the countryside rather than the park; the child with the long flowing curls is a boy (girls always rode side-saddle).

AN IDEAL HUNTER

In the country there was hunting. Although hunting was (and still is) one of the most dangerous of sports, children of both sexes were encouraged to hunt: 'Riding to hounds, like dancing, is one of the accomplishments much better learned at the age when mankind most easily submit to reproof, and are strongly influenced by

41

Fig 18   'A Chip of the Old Block' – a cartoon from *Punch*.

example.'[12] Ponies were even more carefully chosen for the hunting field than for general use. Shetlands evidently passed well for this purpose, for a leading authority on hunting, Digby Collins, specified his ideal hunter thus:

> The withers high and the shoulders long, in order to enable him to rise well at his fences, as well as to clear the obstacles that may come across him, in the shape of ridge and furrow, drains, hillocks, &c.; the hips and pelvis should be broad, with deep back ribs and powerful loins, in order that he may be able to dash his haunches under him at a big jump. I have seen these 'points' intensely developed in a pony 10 hands high.[13]

The Shetlands' sure-footedness must have been another great asset in the hunting field. And as for courage – the 'Punch' cartoon shows a typical juvenile 'thruster' mounted on a Shetland (*see* Fig 18).

THE QUEEN'S PONIES

The cornerstone of the Shetland pony's prestige was royal patronage. Her Majesty Queen Victoria had several Shetlands. Major Cox quotes from letters that were sent in 1864 from Holyrood Palace to a breeder on the Shetland Islands, Mr P. Laurenson of Grenister Farm, Lerwick. Her Majesty had paid a total of £19 7s 6d for 'a small pony' (£4 10s) and 'the chestnut and white pair' (£14 10s), and for three bridles (7s 6d).[14] The Queen was evidently fond of coloured Shetlands, for she had some more at Windsor; these were a pair of duns or creams that were bred by Mr Balfour of Balfour Castle on Shapinsay (in the Orkneys). Her Majesty's Shetlands drew a phaeton in which she took her exercise in Windsor Park. These ponies grew into a royal tradition, and the Queen's daughter, HRH The Princess Victoria, also had a phaeton with a pair of Shetlands (*see* Fig 19). The scale of this picture is a little confusing, but if one takes the Princess as being of middling height the ponies come out at about 40in; they look as if they might be bigger only because the groom is so small (it was for a long time the fashion to employ boys or small men as liveried grooms; they were known as 'tigers'). Note that the ponies are of two different colours (probably chestnut and black), which was thought to make a smarter pair than the matched ones that are almost the rule nowadays; chestnut and grey was also a favoured combination.

Drawn by J. Doyle.   Engraved on wood by E. Babbage.

Fig 19   HRH The Princess Victoria in her phaeton drawn by a pair of Shetland ponies.

There were other Shetlands at Windsor besides these. Sir Walter Gilbey says that they were used 'to do various kinds of work'.[15] Some idea of what sort of work could be done by small ponies in the days before mechanisation and electricity is given by Mr Mackenzie:

> Then much may be claimed for them as general utility ponies, either to those who can afford nothing else, or even at a large country house. With a minimum of care and attention they are always ready for any odd job and are never sick or sorry. As anyone can drive him, the sheltie is turned out whenever there is an errand to run or a parcel to fetch from the station, and when not otherwise employed he can be harnessed to the mowing-machine. At one country house we know, one of his many jobs was to pump water by means of a tread-mill in which he was placed for half an hour every morning. This system filled the cisterns with fresh water each day, and was found infinitely superior to the wind-mill it superseded.[16]

This sounds like hard work, and undoubtedly was, but the life of a Shetland pony at a country house, no matter how many jobs he had to do, was infinitely better than the life led by most of his fellow exiles – down the mines.

THE COAL MINES

In the late 1830s an energetic philanthropist, Lord Ashley, began to campaign for better working conditions in the mines. His efforts led to the passing of the Mines Act 1842, which among other things said that children under the age of ten and women could no longer be employed underground.[17] This was predictably unpopular with the employers, who evaded the law whenever they could, but it led to a dramatic demand for pit ponies. There are three stages in transporting coal out of a mine: from coal-face to haulage road, along haulage road to pit bottom, and from pit bottom to surface. Previously, ponies (not Shetlands) had only been used on the haulage roads, while the coal had been brought from the coal-face by women and children dragging sledges. From 1842 things had to change, and ponies began to work at the face. Smaller ponies were better, because they could get into the narrower seams. Low and strong, Shetland ponies seemed purpose-built for the job, and they were first tried out in a few mines in Co. Durham in the mid 1840s. Their use spread very rapidly, particularly as mine-owners discovered

Fig 20   A pit pony at work. This photograph was taken in the
late 1970s in a colliery in Co. Durham. Pit ponies still work
underground today, but they only haul pit props and other
supplies, not coal. (Photo by courtesy of British Coal.)

that they were actually more economical than human labour had
been: they did more work per day, they had a longer working
lifetime, and they cost less to feed even than the meagre wages of
the women and children. Ponies were so convenient for pit haulage
that seventy years later, by which time mechanisation could well
have been brought in to replace them, there were 73,000 ponies
working in Britain's mines.[18]

The pit pony certainly led a very hard life, but it is true to say that
they were well looked after (simply a matter of economics: a fit pony
can work, an unfit one cannot). Robert Brydon, who was employed
by Lord Londonderry (of whom more in the next chapter) to breed
ponies for the pits, described their work:

It is not overstating the case to say that, on an average, they will
travel over 3,000 miles in the course of a year, and 'shift' as many tons

45

of coal. This is no mean performance when we consider that the work
is done in the black darkness of a coal mine, by a pony 38 inches high,
working in a place very little higher than itself. The amount of work
varies in different collieries; in level pits much more can be accomplished than where the gradients are steep. The lot of the pit pony is
certainly a hard one, but it is not, by any means, the dreadful
existence that many suppose. Their work is hard, but they are well
fed, and the equable temperature of the coal mine keeps them
singularly free from all catarrhal infections, so common in animals
which have to stand the vicissitudes of our British climate. As a rule,
their coats are sleek, and their condition such as anyone with a stud
of hunters would envy. There is a popular belief that ponies down
coal mines soon go blind. This is not so; but loss of sight is not
infrequent as the result of accidental injury, to which ponies, working
in the dark passages, are very liable. That they occasionally are badly
used goes without saying, but generally the Shetland pony, from its
tractable disposition, is a favourite with its driver, the putter boy,
from whom, as a rule, it receives, if rough, at least not unkindly,
treatment . . . Ponies have been known to follow their drivers like
dogs, and to be as dejected as a forsaken maiden when, from any

Fig 21   A Shetland pit pony with his 'horse-keeper'. (Photo by
courtesy of British Coal.)

cause, they are separated from each other. Boys – and big boys, too – have wept for the loss of their ponies, killed in an accident, as though the little Shetland were a human friend.[19]

One can only guess at whether or not the ponies felt horror at being in the darkness all the time. Maybe it was only the Shetland ponies' famous patience that enabled them to endure this unnatural state. Robert Brydon could not 'recall a single instance where a Shetland pony had to be withdrawn from the pits as being wicked or unmanageable – a very frequent occurrence with other breeds.' And what courage it must have required to keep on working in such dangerous conditions. Human workers suffered the most appalling casualty rates – 'between 1861 and 1919 a miner was killed every six hours, seriously injured every two hours and injured badly every two or three minutes'[20] – and there is no reason to think that it was any safer for the ponies.

They were of course stabled underground, too, so that they would never see daylight at all, except for their annual holiday above ground which may have been a distressing rather than a refreshing experience, with the light unaccustomedly bright. Yet paradoxically this state of slavery was the salvation of the Shetland pony as a breed. How this came about will be described in the following chapter.

4

The Founding of the Stud Book

The demand for ponies for the mines had a catastrophic effect on the Shetland Islands. For one thing, it occurred at a time when there was terrible poverty among the islanders after the potato famine. Then the price of wool went up, as the mechanised mills in the north of England got into their stride, which tempted a number of landowners to evict crofters in order to establish sheep-walks.[1] Various schemes were devised to provide employment; these included the building of the first roads in the islands. But the crofters remained on the edge of subsistence, and their ponies were just about the only thing they could sell. Up till the time of the Mines Act of 1842, demand for the ponies was patchy. The ponies going to the aristocrats in England and Scotland were often sent by Shetland gentry, not crofters. The latter would be lucky to make a sale at all. Mr Campbell described how visiting Dutch fishermen would pay to take rides on the ponies, and went on:

> This, together with what Money they [the crofters] receive for their Stockings, is all the Cash they have from one Year's End to the other; unless when some *Dutchmen* fancy any of their Horses, then they chance to make a good Profit, as they will sell a Horse to a *Dutchman* for a Pound, that they cannot sell to their Neighbours for three Half-Crowns.[2]

The unfortunate effect of the unsteady demand was that the crofters would sell which ponies they could, i.e. the best ones. That left them with the poorer stock to breed from, so that the next generation was poorer still. Considering that the ponies were their only saleable asset, it was surprising how badly the crofters managed their breeding, and many knowledgeable commentators had complained of this. 'An absurd custom among the farmers of preserving for stallions . . . the most unpromising of the young of the species' was the verdict of the Highland Society's report in 1801.[3] 'The ponies are now much smaller in size than they were thirty years ago, entirely owing to the fact that all the best and stoutest are exported, and stallions of the most puny size are allowed to go at large' was the opinion recorded in the *New Statistical Account* in 1841.[4]

Matters were made worse by the fact that breeding herds were left to their own devices. All the ponies were turned on to the scattald (common grazings) for the summer, and the mares were served by whatever stallion happened to be around, or were not served at all if there were none. It would have been impossible to draw up the pedigree of any pony. Foals were not weaned in the autumn but left on their dam through their first winter. This had two bad results: the foal was not as well grown the next year as it would have been if fed even on hay, and the mare was unable to carry the next year's foal which would be aborted. Mares, therefore, foaled only every other year.

THE COAL-MINE TRADE

Such was the situation when the Islands were hit by the sudden urgent demand for ponies in the mines. There were perhaps 10,000 ponies on the Islands: suddenly, hundreds of ponies were wanted each year.[5] In 1858 some 400 were bought by a single dealer, and in 1861 over 700 left the islands.[6] Only male ponies went to the mines. (mares would have been equally capable of doing the work but it was thought that keeping mares stabled underground with the entires would lead to trouble). Supposing that the 10,000 ponies were made up of roughly 6,000 mares, 3,000 young stock and 1,000 colts and stallions, one can see what a devastating effect the removal of hundreds of male ponies every year must have had. The dealers would buy any sound pony between the ages of two and twelve, leaving only the unsound and the older horses (these must have been the saving of the breed).[7]

The crofters were in a state of poverty, and now, suddenly, money came to the Islands. Dealers moved in, not just to buy colts and stallions from the crofters but to fix up various arrangements giving them a stake in the booming market. Sometimes the system was 'halvers', under which the dealer provided a brood mare in return for a half-share in her offspring.[8] More often dealers would advance a crofter cash or goods against an expected foal.[9]

Prices leapt up. At the start of the trade, ponies cost £4 10s each including delivery to the colliery; by 1861 they were £10 or £12 in the Islands.[10] Crofters were desperate to get as many foals as possible, and it was not unfair criticism to say that 'the breeders are far too indifferent to the points of a sire, as long as they are foal getters'.

The quality of the ponies went down. So did their numbers. At the same time as the collieries were buying up male ponies, American purchasers were keen to have mares in order to set up studs. Naturally they wanted best-quality animals. Demand from England for riding and harness ponies increased at the same time. By 1871 the population had been reduced to 2,247 'unbroken horses and mares, kept solely for breeding'.[12] Clearly, these numbers could not continue to fulfil the demands of the mine-owners. If 1,500 of the above were mature mares, having a foal every other year, there would be 750 foals each year, of which half would be colts, i.e. 375. This was a crisis; and the first man to recognise it was the Marquis of Londonderry.

LORD LONDONDERRY'S STUD

The Marquis was a mine-owner, whose collieries in Co. Durham had been among the earliest to use Shetland ponies. He was pleased with the work the ponies did, and had no intention of letting the supply dry up, or of settling for the inferior ponies that were coming on to the market. In 1870 he leased the islands of Bressay and Noss, and he employed Mr J.J.R. Meiklejohn to manage the stud there. Mr Robert Brydon was to manage the ponies at Lord Londonderry's stud at Seaham Harbour, Co. Durham. Their brief was to breed ponies with 'as much weight as possible and as near the ground as it can be got.' They had to start by combing through the depleted and weedy herds of the crofters, picking out any ponies that seemed to them to be of the right type or in that direction. They did not mind what colour the ponies, mares or stallions, were if the conformation was right (the Shetland fraternity came to believe that Meiklejohn and Brydon had selected blacks only, as the Londonderry type later turned out to be predominantly black, but this was not so).[13] No expense was spared in buying the foundation stock or in laying out the grounds on the islands. Mares were kept in enclosures on

Bressay, while the stallions and colts had their bachelor quarters on Noss (much the smaller island). Foals were weaned in the autumn, and ran with the rest of the young stock on the hills for the winter, being given hay but not shelter. The mares, also fed on hay in the winter, were grouped into bunches of twelve or fifteen to run with a stallion for the summer.

Breeding began in earnest after a few years, and the whole enterprise was a great success. Through careful selection of the right stocks and a well-planned scheme of inbreeding (breeding a lot more closely than most people would care to nowadays, but scientifically perfectly right), a well-defined type of pony soon emerged, and became known as the Londonderry type. It was just what the Marquis had wanted: heavily made, broad in chest, back and quarters, short in the leg with excellent bone and good round feet. Some had prophesied that with the winter feeding at Bressay the ponies would grow taller than the original stock but, in fact, over the years the average height of the Londonderry ponies went down, as smaller ponies were being selectively bred.

As an enlightened policy, Lord Londonderry allowed the crofters on Bressay to run their mares with some of his stallions, so that the improvements in the breed were spread a little more widely. Dealers realised that better colts would fetch better prices, and took action to invest in improving the crofters' stock. Having bought up all the colts, they would choose for a stallion the best pit type that they could find and put him out on the scattalds to run with the crofters' mares. The owner of the stallion would have first refusal of any foal, so the dealer got the benefit of a supply of decent colts to sell for the mines. The crofter got his price if the foal was a colt, and if it was a filly he had acquired a breeding animal very probably better than her dam. Perhaps she might be sold to America or England.

THE EARLIEST BREEDERS

Other landowners followed Lord Londonderry's example and set up studs in which both stallions and mares were chosen for quality and proper records were kept. Mr John Bruce had ponies in three places – on Mousa Island, at Sumburgh, and on Fair Isle – and he used stallions from one stud on mares at another, to keep the best blood evenly distributed. One of his stallions, the dun Lion, foaled

51

in 1864, became one of the foundation stallions of the Londonderry stud. Several breeders on Unst, traditionally the island with the best ponies, also began to breed systematically. They included Mr Alexander Sandison of Uyeasound and the Marquis of Zetland. Mr Anderson Manson's herd of ponies at Laxfirth, just north of Lerwick, was one of the largest in the islands, and of excellent quality; Messrs John Anderson and Sons owned a lot of land around Hillswick, at the northern end of the Mainland, and their stallions were also available for the crofters' mares.

THE STUD BOOK

These gentlemen fully realised the value of the type of pony they had worked ten or twenty years to establish, and they saw that to form a Shetland Pony Stud-Book Society and keep a register of all ponies in a Stud Book was the only way to protect this asset. The Society was formed in 1890; it was from the outset firmly centred on the Shetland Islands. Of the committee of twelve, six were resident in the Islands, four lived in Scotland, and two were from England; one of these was Robert Brydon, who had, of course, very strong links with the Islands.[14] The first President, appropriately, was the Marquis of Londonderry himself. There were 111 members, most of them crofters.

The first volume of the Stud Book was published in 1891, from the Society's offices in Aberdeen. (Although the Society has always felt the Islands to be its spiritual home, its actual home has been on the mainland). It was the first stud book for a native breed to be published in Britain, but it was able to model its style on the stud books for other breeds, such as the Shire, that had recently been started up. In it were entered 408 mares who had had a foal prior to 1 September 1890, and 48 stallions foaled before 1 January 1886. The criteria for a pony's eligibility were that it was under 42in at four years old and that it had been born in the Shetland Islands, or if it had not, that it was of reputed Shetland origin and had been sired by a pony bred in the Islands.

Difficulties of organisation meant that only a small proportion of the Shetland ponies eligible for it were entered in the first volume. It is an odd fact that there were hardly any from the island of Unst, even though there were numerous keen breeders there. Most of the ponies did not have a recorded pedigree going back for more than a single generation (if that, for there were many cases in which the sire was unknown) but some that came from studs where systematic records had been kept, notably Lord Londonderry's, had two or more generations.

The first volume also included several interesting articles by experts. James Goudie wrote on 'The Early History of the Shetland Pony', J.J.R. Meiklejohn on 'Its Breeding and Management', and Robert Brydon on 'Employment After Leaving Shetland'. In this last article, Brydon reflects on the importance of the pit-pony market, comparing the present situation with that of 1851, when thirty male ponies three to five years old were sold to collieries in Durham at £4 10s delivered:

> Since then the ponies have increased to an enormous extent. Average yearlings are now worth, in the north of England, £15 per head; two-year-olds, £18; and older ponies are scarcely obtainable. The price is governed in a great degree by the size. The smaller they are – *coeteris paribus* – the more money they are worth. A good four-year-old, 9.2, will fetch, on an average, £10 more than one five or six inches higher. This is, no doubt, partly owing to fancy, but chiefly to the small ponies being available for work in thin coal seams where larger ones cannot enter. The sheltie being the smallest breed of ponies (and, so far as I am aware, the only breed which boasts of ponies under ten hands), it follows that they have the market all to themselves.
>
> The wisdom of limiting the height of ponies admissible to the Stud-Book to 10.2 and under cannot be too highly commended, as it will tend to make breeders more careful in the selection and mating of their mares. When Shetland ponies are above 10.2, they come into competition with Welsh and foreign ponies, and the price suffers accordingly.

It could not have been more clearly put: the purpose of the Stud Book was to keep the size of the ponies down, because only in that way could their market position be maintained. Thus it came about that the demands of the coalmining trade ensured the survival of the Shetland pony as it originally was and as it still is today. Without that demand and without Lord Londonderry's efforts, Shetland ponies would very probably have drifted away from original type, through breeding from larger ponies and also through crosses with other breeds. This is, in fact, what did happen in America, where ponies were not used in the pits and therefore did not have to be bred to small size (*see* Chapter 11).

THE LONDONDERRY TYPE

The Londonderry type became in this way *the* type for the breed. Ponies of Londonderry type were overwhelmingly successful in the show ring. In 1892, the first year that Highland and Agricultural Society gave its recognition to Shetland ponies by providing classes for them at their annual show, the Marquis took first prize in each of the three classes. This sort of success continued: at the twelve shows of the Highland and Agricultural Society held between 1900 and 1911 there were 116 first and second prizes awarded in the Shetland classes, of which 114 were won by ponies sired by stallions from the Londonderry stud.[17] The type was not without its critics, however. The Douglases commented:

> Many of the most substantial and characteristic ponies of the 'Londonderry' strain are short and straight in shoulder and wholly lacking in withers. Such ponies as these may be useful in the coal-pits, but they are useless above ground.[18]

This extremely harsh criticism is hard to understand when one looks at the photographs of the ponies concerned. The quality of these early pictures is not good, but the great founding stallions – Jack 16, Odin 32, Thor 83 – certainly do *not* appear to have straight shoulders and no withers.

THE LONDONDERRY BREEDING SYSTEM

It is worth looking at how the Londonderry plan of inbreeding worked. The key figure is the stallion, Jack 16. Only one photograph of him exists, in which he is standing up to his fetlocks in snow, his head held by a bearded man (Mr Meiklejohn perhaps); he looks a great character. He was bought at the outset of the Londonderry stud, a colt of unknown breeding. He was black, and 40in high (on the tall side for a Londonderry type). The Douglases approved of him, at least: 'a short-backed and close-coupled horse of remarkable bone and substance, finely proportioned, and with a bold and upright carriage'.[19] Jack lived to be thirty years old, and worked at stud all his life. He had three outstanding sons, and the four of them together make up the main strand in the Londonderry blood line.

The sons were Odin 32, who looked very like his father but was

Fig 22 The legendary Jack 16, the most important stallion in
the Londonderry stud.

Fig 23 Odin.

somewhat smaller at 38in (his dam, Nugget, was sired by Tom Thumb 44, a 34in pony who was brought back from the mines to the stud to breed down the size); Laird of Noss 20, another black 38in, somewhat more lightly built than his brother Odin; and Lord of the Isles 26, black, smallest of the three at 36in but the most thickset in build.

The importance that the Londonderry breeders attached to Jack and his sons can be seen from the facts that Jack was the sire or grandsire of one-third of the mares used in the stud and that Jack and his sons sired 248 out of the first 490 foals registered as produce of the stud; a further 160 were by Jack's grandsons. The daughters of Jack and of his sons were, in the majority of cases, mated to either their own sire or to one of their brothers (full or half).

But there was another male blood line, that of Prince of Thule 36. A brown 36in high, he was of a type quite different from Jack; the Douglases had heard him described as 'a pony of exquisite quality, with a small thoroughbred head, prominent wide-set reddish hazel eyes, and an exceedingly fine muzzle'.[20] They saw in him the only representative in the Londonderry stud of what they called the 'Oriental' type (*see* page 24) as opposed to Jack's line which was of

Fig 24   Prince of Thule.

Fig 25   Bellman.

the Scandinavian type. Prince of Thule was used on daughters of
Jack and also, particularly, daughters of Odin, perhaps to put back
in some quality that might otherwise have been sacrificed in the
search for weight-near-the-ground. This was also done with Prince
of Thule's most famous son, Oman 33, another brown but only 34in
high who had inherited his father's quality and good action.

The system, then, was to inbreed as closely as possible to the Jack
line, with occasional out crosses to the Prince of Thule line, the
resulting mares being put back to the Jack line, *not* to their sire's. It
was also a policy to put the mares to a different horse nearly every
year. As an example, the foundation mare Darling 174 (by Jack) had
her first three foals by the three different brothers.

It was brilliantly successful breeding, and the Douglases do not
overstate when they say that the results were 'a degree of breed
improvement which is perhaps without a parallel'.[21] By the late
1890s the future seemed rosy: the breed had been saved, the Stud
Book was established, sales were still high. The Shetland pony
world was shattered in 1899 by the news that Lord Londonderry
had failed to negotiate the renewal of his lease of Bressay and Noss,
and that his whole stud was to be sold up.

5

The Decline and Rise of the Shetland Pony

The sale of the Londonderry stud, at the very end of the century, on 7 September 1899, marked the end of an era for Shetland ponies. The sale was held not on the Islands but at Seaham Harbour, Co. Durham (most of the purchasers were expected to be from the mainland). The Marquis was not present, but the Marchioness laid on a lavish luncheon for the buyers.

One hundred and fifty ponies were sold that afternoon. The total sum realised was 3067½ guineas (£3221).[1] It is difficult to convert accurately into the present-day value of the pound, but the equivalent is not less than £150,000 total.[2] The average price paid for a pony was just over 20 guineas (£21), present equivalent about £1,000. The top price was 125 guineas (£131), equivalent to over £6,500. These were astonishingly high prices, and the people who paid them were not breeders in the Islands (only a dozen ponies went back to the Shetlands after the sale[3]) but gentry who had already established studs of ponies in Scotland and England.

The gentleman who paid the top price, a Colonel Fraser of Shropshire, soon disappeared from view, and the filly herself, Fancy Fair, was never heard of again. The people who paid the next-highest price – 80 guineas (present equivalent, £4,200) for a three-year-old filly, Sea Serpent – were very important indeed in the Shetland world. They were the Ladies Estella and Dorothea Hope, daughters of the 6th Earl of Hopetoun, of Hopetoun House, Linlithgow. They first had Shetland ponies when they were still girls, and had been breeding for several years when the Stud Book was established. They were founder members of the Society, though they had already moved to southern England. Their breeding lines followed closely on those of Lord Londonderry, from whom they bought their first important stallion, the elegant Prince of Thule, whom they acquired at an earlier draft sale at Seaham Harbour at the advanced age of 22. Three years later they also bought his son, Oman, who replaced his father (still standing at stud at the age of twenty-nine) when he broke his back in a fight in 1899, not long before the Londonderry dispersal sale. On that occasion, they bought another stallion, Jack's son Odin, for whom they paid 52 guineas (£2,730), even though he was nineteen years old. Lady Estella and Lady Dorothea bought twelve ponies at the 1899 sale, which was almost the last time they brought ponies into their stud, all later breeding being done entirely from their existing stock.

The ladies' substantial purchases were outnumbered by those of Mr Robert Mackenzie, another founder member of the Stud-Book Society. He owned the Earlshall stud in Fife, and at the Londonderry dispersal sale he bought fifteen ponies, all female.

His Earlshall stud was one of the largest, and after a few years he was registering over thirty foals a year. His ponies were taller on average than the Londonderry stock, and he was particularly interested in breeding colours. He brought in a grey stallion from the Islands to get foals of that colour, and also bred himself the most important of all the chestnut sires in the breed, Emillius of Earlshall. Various other breeders, already well established and belonging to the Stud-Book Society, took the opportunity to acquire Londonderry ponies, but over a third of the ponies sold disappeared completely from the annals of the breed.

A BUOYANT MARKET

The first decade of the century was a good time for the Shetland breeders. Demand was brisk, not so much for ponies for the pits but for riding and harness ponies for home and export. The number of breeders registering their ponies in the Stud Book reflects this buoyant market: in 1901 there were 114 (70 living in the islands, 44 elsewhere) and in 1913 there were 249 (150 in the islands, 99 elsewhere).[4] Many of the studs with great names that are found in the pedigrees of today's best ponies were started up at that time.

Mr Mungall's stud at Transy, Dunfermline, was already in existence at the time of the Londonderry dispersal, and he bought a few ponies there. He bred along Londonderry lines, being interested particularly in driving ponies. (The present-day Transy stud, owned by Mr Dougal Dick, is the direct continuation of this stud, and the emphasis on performance has been maintained.)

Other important breeders of this time include Dr Douglas (who with his wife wrote the early book on Shetland ponies); he strove to breed a lighter type than the classic Londonderry pony, although when he started his stud in 1902 it was mainly with Londonderry-bred foundation stock. Mrs Hobart of Southampton was another to breed along the same lines. She purchased several stallions from Lady Estella Hope, and ponies from her stud were successfully shown both in hand and in harness. Mrs Houldsworth of Kirkbride, Ayrshire, began to breed in 1909, founding her stud on a stallion of Dr Douglas's breeding (and therefore ultimately of Londonderry blood). She concentrated on the classic Londonderry type, which was still being bred at Kirkbride up until the death of her son Sir Reginald Houldsworth in 1989.

Just before the 1914–18 war, Mr Kerr of Harviestoun took up breeding, basing his stud on Transy and Earlshall stock. His breeding struck just the right note, and has had a considerable influence on later breeding of show ponies. Many of the black ponies winning in the ring now have Harviestoun ancestry not too far back in their pedigrees.

THE OTHER STUD BOOK

During the boom years of the Shetland pony trade, the Council of the Stud-Book Society decided to close the Stud Book; that is, it would from that time become impossible to register any pony whose parents were not already recorded in the Stud Book. This happened in 1905.[5] But by 1908 the situation was causing great difficulties for the crofter – breeders; they had not bothered to register their mares with the Stud-Book Society and now they found, to their chagrin, that they were unable to export stock to Canada and America, both of which countries required incoming ponies to have registration papers.

Two things happened: some crofters took the bureaucratic route and got the Zetland County Council to write to the Stud-Book Society asking that the Stud Book should be reopened. The Stud-Book Society dragged its feet. Meanwhile others took direct action by setting up a rival organisation, the Shetland Islands Stud Book Society. Conditions for entering a pony in this Stud Book were much less stringent than for the original Stud Book. Any pony belonging to a person living in the Islands could be entered, and the pony could be taller (43in at four years old, 41in at three years old – which might well make bigger than 43in at maturity). This was good enough for the Canadian Board of Agriculture, who recognised the new Society; many ponies were exported under its papers. Luckily America did not follow suit. These events brought the original Stud-Book Society to its senses, and they reopened their Book in 1910, inspecting and registering 427 new mares in the single year. Not surprisingly the rival Stud Book simply withered away.

The impact of the First World War on Shetland ponies was admittedly not as severe as on many other humans and animals, but it did mark the beginning of their worst times. During the war itself, demand for ponies dropped dramatically. Some were still wanted in the mines, but no one was buying ponies for pleasure; worst hit of all was the export market. What a change from the days just before the war when the two rival Stud Books were racing each other for the transatlantic trade; now things were so bad that no one knew where to sell a pony, and everyone was overstocked. The most notable casualty of this slump was the Hillswick stud run by the Andersons, founder members of the Stud-Book Society. They had been breeders themselves on a large scale, had put good stallions out on the scattalds for the crofters, and had bought in foals to sell on. In 1911 they sold over a hundred ponies off the Islands, in 1913 over 130 – but in 1919 they went bust. They were followed in the early 1920s by Mr Sandison of Unst, another of the leading lights of the Society, and in 1927 Mr Bruce disposed of his ponies from Mousa, Sumburgh, and Fair Isle.

SHETLANDS OUT OF FAVOUR

Shetland ponies ceased to be fashionable in England. Although horse-drawn transport was still important everywhere, the car had made its entrance and was vastly more interesting to people who wanted to cut a dash. Shetlands fell out of favour as riding ponies for children, too. There may have been several reasons for this. They no longer had the cachet of royal patronage, as they had done in Victoria's reign: King George V's children were no longer little and the royal household had no need of small ponies. Welsh ponies had risen in popularity, and the fashion for children's ponies was for this leggier type. Many books on riding written in the 1920s and 1930s have a derisive comment to make about Shetland ponies: 'I omit from riding ponies the Shetland, for he is too small for practical purposes', wrote no less an authority than R.S. Summerhayes.[6] Or worse:

> I do not like Shetland ponies for children, and apologise to Shetland breeders for this statement. It may be that I have had unfortunate experience with them, but I do not think the breed is docile, and as they age they get too broad on the back.[7]

A few devoted breeders carried on, and the quality of their stock was not only as good as that seen in the heyday of the Londonderry stud but even better, as the 'riding type' as described by the Douglases (*see* page 56) became more common. These breeders continued to support the Stud-Book Society and to exhibit their ponies at the few shows that had classes for them, but the prices that Shetland ponies were fetching in the late 1920s and 1930s were such that the breeders were doing it for love not money. Cox remarks: 'By 1927 mares and fillies were scarcely saleable.'[8]

When Mr Mackenzie retired he dispersed his famous Earlshall stud. The dispersal sale was held on 23 November 1932, and Messrs Crow were the auctioneers as they had been at the Londonderry dispersal. The results could hardly have been more different. Mr Mackenzie sold ninety-six ponies for a total of £643 18s 3d, and the average price was only £6 14s 1d. The value of money had perhaps halved since the beginning of the century, so the equivalents are £16,090, total, and £160 average price.[9] These were absolutely top-class ponies, the finest in the breed, but the prices they were fetching was only about one-sixth of what they would have done at the Londonderry sale. Prices were even worse elsewhere; breeding stock could be had for £3 or £4 a head in England. Demand for pit ponies was much reduced as a result of the general slowing-down of the manufacturing industry during the Depression, but male ponies could still be sold for a modest price to go down the mines. Mares and fillies from the Islands were completely unsaleable, as their value was less than the cost of shipping them to Aberdeen.

The number of ponies being registered in the Stud Books went down to a fraction of what it had been before the First World War. In 1914 the Stud Book registered 562 foals, 135 mares, 49 inspected mares, and 51 stallions; the figures in 1935 were 111 foals, 28 mares, 2 inspected mares and 6 stallions.

BREEDERS UNDAUNTED

Among the faithful breeders were the following. Lady Estella Hope, whose sister Dorothea had died in 1927, moved from Kent to Sussex, to South Park which gave its name to her stud. The stud was very carefully managed, and achieved the remarkable success of establishing two lines of ponies, different in size but with very similar elegance and quality. The name South Park is now more associated with miniature ponies and indeed these ponies are of a most striking type which has been of great influence and benefit at the small end of the breed. But the Ladies Hope were always equally interested in larger ponies, and bred very good ponies in the size around 37in or 38in, black as well as coloured. Attractive colour has been a hallmark of the South Park strain, going right back to their legendary foundation mare, Hoplemuroma, who was roan. (Her feats in harness will be mentioned in Chapter 8.) Very many of the roan ponies seen in the ring today have South Park ancestry; virtually all of the roan miniatures do. Another characteristic of South Park colouring is white socks, sometimes with a narrow flash of white on the belly; the effect when the pony is in harness is most attractive (*see* Fig 27).

Fig 26   Coronado, bred by Lady Estella Hope, an example of her larger type of pony.

Fig 27 The Duchess of Devonshire driving Floristan, a typical
South Park miniature pony.

Mr Mungall of Transy continued to breed and show; his confidence in the future of the breed was unshakeable, in spite of the
difficult times. When he died in 1936 his daughter, Mrs William
Dick, took over and carried on with the same confidence. Mr Kerr of
Harviestoun also went on with his breeding and showing. Mrs
Duffus, who had begun her stud in about 1910 and had achieved
extraordinary success in the show ring, particularly with her black
stallion Dibblitz of Penniwells, sold all her ponies in 1932.

Several important new studs were started in the 1920s and 1930s.
Probably the most influential was that of Mrs Maurice Cox, wife of
the authority Major Cox. Her stud was founded at Marshwood in
Dorset, and only moved to Kirkcudbrightshire after the Second
World War. She aimed for, and achieved, a type of pony remarkable
for its free action and prolific mane and tail. Another highly im-
portant stud was founded by Miss A. Ritchie at Broadshade,
Aberdeenshire; her Netherley ponies were more like the original
Londonderry type, black and with great substance. Mrs Atkinson's
Felbridge stud in Surrey specialised in coloured ponies. Based on
Earlshall blood lines, her breeding achieved the sort of quality
usually associated with black ponies but in chestnut and grey
ponies.

Fig 28   A Netherley pony: Merry Minion of Netherley, owned
by Mrs M. Brooker. The driver is Philippa Dobson, the groom
Yvonne Nicol.

Fig 29   A Felbridge pony: Santolina of Felbridge, owned by
the late Miss Nan French and driven by her stud groom Cecil
Monk. (The other pony is Mrs Swannack's home-bred
Midnight of Woodbury.)

THE EFFECTS OF THE WAR

The Second World War dealt another blow to these studs. Wartime regulations were imposed upon the use of land, which had to be turned over wherever possible to food production. Shetland ponies, though they made themselves useful as far as possible with jobs round the farms, could only be considered a luxury (heaven forbid that they should be thought of as food), so the numbers in the studs went down still further as ponies were replaced with sheep. Some studs lost their grazing altogether; sometimes, the breeders were able to board out a few ponies with friends until better times came and breeding could start again. This happened with the Transy stud, which was not able to set up again until 1954. Major Cox recalls that of the fifty ponies at the Marshwood stud at the beginning of the war only seven were left at the end.[10]

And yet the breed survived. Indeed the post-war economic recovery all round the world benefited Shetland ponies as much as anybody else. Suddenly people wanted riding ponies for their children again, and Shetland ponies were back in favour for this.

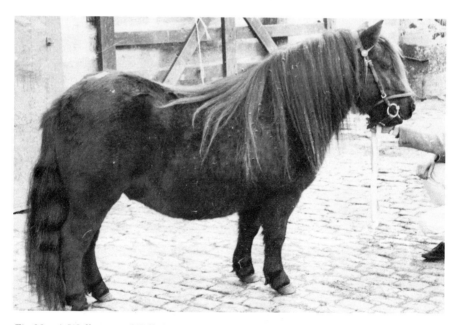

Fig 30   A Wells pony: Wells Vanita at two years old (owned by Mrs D.V.M. Howell).

Fig 31 Elector of Annwood, who combines four of the best blood lines. He is by Merlin of Luckdon out of Wells Elenora; Merlin was by Thunder of Marshwood out of Mystic of Netherley. Elector is owned and bred by Mrs O'Brien.

Received opinion in equestrian circles was that the Shetland virtues of gentleness, sure-footedness, and hardiness were worth having after all, and one of the breed's keenest supporters (though not herself a breeder) was Miss Glenda Spooner, founder of Ponies of Britain: 'They are excellent and reliable, while in harness their speed and endurance is astonishing.'[11] The Americans and Canadians once more came over to buy Shetland ponies, in dozens rather than hundreds, but as before they wanted quality and would pay for it.

POST-WAR STUDS

A number of new breeders established studs in this more cheerful climate for Shetlands. Mr H.P. Sleigh, whose father had had a stud before the First World War, began his Wells stud in 1948. The importance of this stud cannot be overstated; breeding closely and aiming for the short-coupled Londonderry pony, Mr Sleigh has had the most phenomenal success in the show ring. Wells ponies won the championship at the Royal Highland Show twenty-one times, and the Royal (English) fifteen times. Often enough in the years

Fig 32   An Ebony pony: Ebony Poppy, owned by Mr and Mrs
G. Hughes. (Photo by courtesy of *Congleton Chronicle*.)

when Mr Sleigh has not shown the champion, the title has gone to a
pony bred from Wells stock. Other highly important studs dating
from the late 1940s were those of Mr T.H.F. Myles of Fife (whose
stud prefix is Highfield), Mr I. Dishington of Kendal (Lakeland),
Miss E.M. Glasier of Tetbury (Avening), Miss E. Smith of Scalloway
(Berry), and Mrs S.C. Swannack (Woodbury).

More studs continued to be established in the 1950s. Among the
names that are important because their ponies figure in the breeding
of the best ponies today are: Mrs K. Amers of Moretonhampstead,
Devon (Luckdon), Mrs Nancy Ducker of Reading (Littlestoke), Miss
Amy Edge of Kendal (Hutton), Mr W. Shillibeer of Yelverton,
Devon (Lakehead), Mrs Greaves of Dumfries (Ebony), the Misses
Salter and French of Guildford (Hurtwood), Major N. Hambro, first
of Rugby later of Exford, Somerset (Winwick), Mrs M.J. King of
Painswick, Glos. (Donnachaidh), Mrs E. Hyde of Callander, Perth-
shire (Braes of Greenock), and Mr and Mrs R. Gosling of Stowmar-
ket (Wetherden).

In the mid 1950s demand from America shot up (*see* Chapter 11).
In the Shetland Islands something of the problem that had occurred
in the 1850s repeated itself a century later; sudden very heavy

Fig 33   A Braes of Greenock pony: Braes of Greenock Bonny
Boy. (Note his Highland friend.)

demand for ponies was tempting the island breeders to sell off their
best animals (prices were very good, particularly from the American
trade) so that they were left with nothing worth breeding from. The
Department of Agriculture for Scotland saw the danger before the
Stud-Book Society did, and they set up a scheme to lend good
stallions to the crofters. For the first few years these stallions were
kept in an enclosure, and mares had to be brought to them. This
was a troublesome business, particularly as most of the mares were
half-wild and hard to catch, and the scheme was not at first a
success. By 1956 the Society realised that it had to take action, so
they co-operated with the Department of Agriculture to set up a
new scheme with serious intentions. Stallions were to be selected by
the Society and would be turned out on scattalds so that all the
mares there would benefit. At the same time the grazing laws were
altered so that it was not permitted to run a colt over a year old on
the scattalds unless it had been approved by the Society and was
registered in the Stud Book. The improvement in the quality of
island-bred ponies was immediate.

The Society also realised that breeders on the Islands were at a
considerable disadvantage in the market in that they had to get their

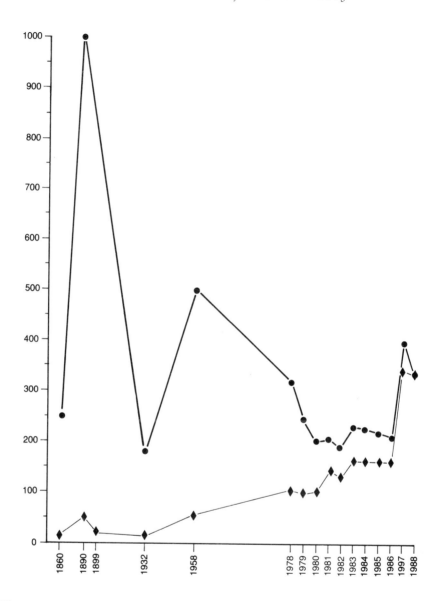

Fig 34 The price of Shetland ponies. The bottom line shows
the actual price in pounds at the time, the top line the value
translated into today's pounds. For the past ten years, the
price given is the average at the Reading sale.

stock at their own expense to the annual sale in Aberdeen, or sell at a discount to a dealer. The first Shetland pony sale in the Islands was held at Baltasound in October 1958, and it was a spectacular success. The top-priced pony was a yearling filly who fetched 116 guineas (£121); filly foals averaged over 50 guineas. With the value of money at least ten times what it is now, one can see that these prices were back at the heights reached at the Londonderry sale. The Age of Gold had come again.

6

Showing In Hand

The Shetland ponies of the new Golden Age went into the show ring, in their hundreds. The old hands who are still showing now look back on those days with unashamed nostalgia. There were far fewer classes for Shetlands than there are now, with only the very largest shows having more than two, but the standard both of the ponies themselves and the professionalism of the people showing them was very high.

Many more top-quality studs had been founded in the early 1960s, and these new breeders were keen exhibitors. Among these were the Duchess of Devonshire, of Chatsworth, Derbyshire, Mrs G. Knight of Wantage, Berkshire (stud prefix Lockinge), Mrs D.W.J. O'Brien of Nutley, Sussex (Annwood), Mrs A.W.R. Houghton of Sysonby, Leicestershire, Mrs P. Lory of Basingstoke, Hants (Southley), Mrs E. House of Over Stowey, Somerset (Bincombe), Mrs D. Page of Swallowfield, Berkshire, Miss J. Bolton of Stoke-on-Trent (Oakamoor), Mrs N.C. Selway of Stanhoe, Norfolk, Mrs K.M. Lee of Kinoulton, Nottinghamshire (Drakelaw), and Mr and Mrs Church of Hadlow Down, Sussex (Nashes).

THE NEWBURY RACECOURSE SHOW

These, and the earlier breeders named in the last chapter, were the people who were showing at the time when the first all-Shetland show was held. Organised by Mrs Knight, the show took place in August 1964 at Newbury Racecourse. There were ten in-hand classes: yearling colt or filly, two- or three-year-old colt, two- or three-year-old filly, mare, foal, two- or three-year-old filly (coloured), mare (coloured), miniature colt, filly or mare, novice, and progeny group. (There were also one driving and two ridden classes.) This range of classes gave every breeder something to go for, and the show was immensely popular.

Fig 35   The Newbury Racecourse show. Lionel Hamilton-
Renwick's Longmead Glamour Girl winning the Under-34in
youngstock class. (Photo by Clive Hiles.)

All the old hands look back on the Newbury all-Shetland shows
with happy memories: 'Oh, it was all such fun then!' 'A show was a
real social event.' Mrs Knight ran the Newbury Racecourse shows
for nine years with great success. The all-Shetland show became a
two-day event in 1970, with twenty-one classes. The impetus that
this show gave to Shetland ponies was of enormous value. After the
last of Mrs Knight's shows, Mr Lionel Hamilton-Renwick took over,
and he ran an all-Shetland show at Huntingdon Racecourse in 1974
and again in 1975. By that time, the idea of shows just for Shetlands,
with riding and driving classes as well, had well and truly caught
on. In 1975 there were eight Shetland-only shows: Huntingdon
Racecourse (thirteen in-hand classes), the Midland Shetland Pony
show at Lilford Park, Northants (sixteen classes), Roby Stud (four
classes), Goodwood (six classes), Steeple Barton, Oxon (twelve
classes), Red Rice, Hants (eleven classes), the Autumn Shetland
Pony Show at Wellington Country Park, Berks (five classes), and

Unst (ten classes). The Unst Show was the first all-Shetland show in the Islands, having started in 1971 with seven classes. There was also the all-Shetland show that Mrs Knight ran at her home, Lockinge Manor, after she gave up the Newbury Racecourse show; this was a unique show, concentrating on riding and driving classes, but also including one in-hand class for mares or geldings suitable for riding.

At the time when the first all-Shetland show began, there were only about 150 in-hand classes for Shetlands in total, generally just two or three classes per show; shows like the Royal Highland or the Royal with five or six Shetland classes were few and far between. But ten years later there were seventy-seven in-hand classes at the breed shows alone, and about 200 classes at the general shows.

INTER-BREED CHAMPIONSHIPS

Winning ponies at the general shows went into competition against the winning ponies of other breeds for the Mountain and Moorland

Fig 36   The good old days: The Royal Show 1968. Betty Cox showing a Marshwood filly.

Fig 37   Chatsworth Easter Bonnet. (Photo by Jones
Photographers.)

championship. On the whole, they were not very successful; Shetlands have such a very different outline than the other breeds that
perhaps non-Shetland judges found it hard to compare them fairly.
One exception to this was the outstandingly beautiful filly Chatsworth Easter Bonnet, bred by The Lady Sophia Cavendish (ten-
year-old daughter of the Duke and Duchess of Devonshire). Easter
Bonnet was Reserve Champion Mountain and Moorland pony at
the Ponies of Britain Show in 1966, in the highest quality of company. She was also twice Supreme Champion at the Newbury all-
Shetland show.

The only Shetland pony to make a mark in the Lloyds Bank In-
Hand Championship, which was a national championship for all
sizes of horses and ponies and ran through the 1970s and 1980s, was
Mrs House's classic type of stallion, Bincombe Venture. He was
second in the finals at Wembley in 1980, and qualified again in 1982
when he came third.

Fig 38   Bincombe Venture.

Fig 39   Father loses championship to son: Lakeland Lightning
congratulates Eastlands Lightning on winning the title at the
Ponies of Britain Stallion Show. (Photo by Carol Gilson.)

THE SOCIETY'S OWN SHOW

Surprisingly, in view of the great interest in in-hand showing, the Shetland Pony Stud-Book Society did not hold an official show for the breed until 1982. The first show was held on 25 September 1982 at Park Hall, Lancs, and had twenty-four in-hand classes which attracted some 250 entries. The show has been held every year since then, at a different venue each time. It was held in Scotland for the first time in 1985, at Kinross. For the centenary year, 1990, the breed show will return to Scotland, to the Royal Highland Show's ground near Edinburgh.

More Shetland-only shows were started in the early 1980s, and the North of England Shetland Show (held in July) and the South Wales Shetland Show (held in August) are major events in the calendar. Berry Barton, Devonshire and Hermitage, Shropshire, are also well supported Shetland shows. The older shows such as the Midland and the Autumn Shetland shows continue to thrive.

Fig 40   Hose Vanesto, bred and owned by Mesdames J.A. and J.R. Stevenson. This pony had a highly successful show career in the 1980s, including winning the breed's premier award, the championship at the Royal Highland Show.

The showing scene at the beginning of the 1990s is in very healthy shape, in terms of numbers of shows and classes at least. The number of shows affiliated to the Shetland Pony Stud-Book Society in 1989 was over 120, with a total of classes in the region of 750.

HOW TO SHOW YOUR PONY

Hints on what and what not to do to show a pony in hand have been printed time and again in one place or another, in the Shetland Pony Stud-Book Society Magazine and elsewhere, but the standard of presentation and behaviour is still uneven so perhaps it is worth laying out the main points again.

Preparation for showing starts during the winter preceding the summer showing season. That is when you will feed your show pony carefully to make sure that it is in the right condition for the show ring. Take the pony out for exercise during the winter to get some muscle on; if it is a stallion or yeld mare you can exercise in harness, if a colt or filly just walk the pony out. The winter is also the time to school the pony to do what is required in the show ring. Far the most important part of this is to learn to walk and trot out freely. It improves the appearance of a pony one hundred per cent if it can trot with its head correctly carried and its stride free and long, and the pony cannot possibly do this unless you can let it go on a long rein. If you are hanging on to it so that its head is pulled round to the side the pony does not stand a chance. The pony must also learn to 'stand up', that is to say to stand with its head fairly high and its weight on all four feet, hind feet well back. This is less important than being able to trot out well, and it is as well not to overdo it; an exaggerated stance is not required. It is also necessary for your pony to be prepared to stand still in the line-up for a long time without fidgeting and annoying the other ponies, so practise standing still.

When spring comes, your problem will be to stop the pony getting a thick layer of fat all over that nice muscle you have carefully built up. Some sort of rationing will have to be applied, probably consisting of keeping the pony in for a fair amount of time. If you have a mare that you are going to show with her foal, you need not worry about the fat. Let her eat. Teach the foal to be led, as you cannot risk having a foal running loose around a showground.

For the cosmetic aspects of showing, it is lucky that the conven-

Fig 41   Derek O'Brien teaching a colt to stand up.

tions for mountain and moorland ponies require very little interference with the natural state of the animal. The pony's head looks a better shape if you trim off the long hairs growing along the jawbone, but trim nothing else. You will of course have had the pony's feet trimmed to a good shape, or it may be shod because of riding or driving commitments. It is now perfectly acceptable to show a Shetland pony in-hand with shoes on, though there used to be a prejudice against it from persons who believed that shoes were only ever used on Shetlands to correct faulty action.

On the day before the show get the pony clean. The old-fashioned, and the best, way to clean a pony is with a body brush, but as it is extremely hard work (worse on a Shetland because it is so low down) most people now shampoo the pony instead. Brush the mane and tail really thoroughly – these are the Shetland's great glories. Then you will have to put the pony in a box with clean bedding for the night, and hope it will not pass the time by getting itself dirty again.

SHOW TACK

After you have dealt with your pony, you must clean your show tack. Once again, this is fairly simple for Shetlands. There is no need for a filly up to the age of three to wear a bit; for them a slip like a

Fig 42 Full stallion gear, worn by Kirkbride Harbour, owned
and bred by the late Colonel Sir Reginald Houldsworth.
(Photo by R. Clapperton, Photographer, Selkirk.)

close-fitting headcollar looks good, and this will also do for a
yearling colt, though an older colt will need a bit. Mares are very
often shown in a bridle, but it is not necessary, and a good leather
headcollar or slip is fine. Stallions are only very occasionally shown
with a roller and side-reins; many people do not think it suits the
Shetland outline. A foal looks best in a leather foal-slip, but it could
wear a white halter. In all cases, your lead rein can be either leather
or white webbing. In no circumstances (apart from the foal just
mentioned), can you show a pony with anything but leather on its
head: nylon headcollars, no matter how clean, are not on.

The last thing you do on the day before the show is to check how
far you have to go and what time your class is; you absolutely must
get there in good time. Reckon to be at the showground at least an
hour before your class.

On the day, keep calm. You have arrived at the ground in good
time. Get your pony out of the box and walk it round a little to let it
get over the journey; if it has broken into a sweat while travelling,
walk it round for as long as it takes for it to cool down. Then tie it up
and spruce it up for the ring; as it was absolutely spotless only last
night, this should not be too difficult. Brush mane and tail again,
polish coat with a cloth and oil hooves. Then spruce yourself up:

Fig 43   Last minute pre-
parations: brushing the
tail. Mrs Turvill and her
filly Knock Good Luck.

Fig 44   Oiling the hooves: Chris Stevens with Vandal of
Catchpool.

you can dress in more or less any style you like – riding gear, summer frock, city suit – provided that it is neat, tidy, and decent. *No* jeans, *no* strapless tops, *no* shorts. Do not forget your number, which at most shows is worn by you (it is easier for the onlookers to read if it is round your waist rather than your arm) but is sometimes worn by the pony.

RING MANNERS

Get to the collecting ring in good time, and from now on, do everything that the steward tells you. Once you are in the ring you walk round, and then trot; make sure that you have plenty of room so that your pony can show off its action, and if you really do have to overtake the pony in front of you, go round the side away from the judge (because it is bad manners to obscure the judge's view of someone else's pony). Then you will be asked to walk again, and the judge will choose which ponies to call in. Remember that this is only his or her provisional choice and that all is not lost if you are not called in first. Above all do *not* try to come in to the line when you have not been called; the steward will signal to you perfectly clearly if you are wanted, and it is embarrassing for everybody when you have to be moved if you have pushed in.

Fig 45 The time for a chat is in the collecting ring: scene at the Surrey County Show.

Fig 46   The final line-up: a class at the Spring Shetland Show.

Once you are in the line concentrate on your pony. It is not a good time for a chat, tempting though it may be. You have to keep the pony awake so that it will look good when its turn comes (or if it is excitable, you must try to keep it calm). It is also a good idea to keep it standing well, because very often the judge will glance at the ponies waiting in the line and form an impression either good or bad.

When it is your turn to come up in front of the judge the rule is: do not speak unless you are spoken to. All the judge is likely to want to know is how old the pony is. It is the height of bad form to offer bits of information about the pony's breeding or how many prizes it has won. (Not only must you not say this directly to the judge, you must not cause him or her to overhear it by saying it loudly to someone else.)

Now is the time to make the most of your pony's ability to trot out properly. Trot away in a straight line and go a good long way before turning. Keep the pony in the judge's view, i.e. go round the outside, and trot back equally straight, going on past the judge. The trotting out is the most important part of the judging procedure, and you can easily go up or down several places according to how well your pony shows itself off.

When the final choice is made, be sporting. If you have won, somebody else has lost and probably feels bad about it. If you have lost, well, there is always another day. The judge is always right, because only the judge has had the opportunity of seeing all the ponies from the same point of view. It is perfectly alright to seek out the judge at the end of the day and ask why your pony did not do better; you will almost certainly learn something.

7

Shetland Ponies Under Saddle

Shetlands as riding ponies are busier now than ever before. At the time when the in-hand showing boom began, in the 1960s, opportunities for ridden Shetlands consisted of little more than appearing in the Leading Rein class alongside flashier looking creatures of Welsh or even thoroughbred breeding. Shetlands seldom did well. There were also the ridden Mountain and Moorland classes at major shows but again judges generally preferred a more lightly built breed, whatever the merits of the Shetland candidates. Serious breeders did not usually bother to show their ponies under saddle at all.

Right from the start the breed shows have included several ridden classes. The 1964 Newbury Racecourse show had two classes, Leading Rein (riders seven or under) and First Ridden (riders eleven or under); at last Shetlands could compete with one another and get a fair chance. The later breed shows carried on the tradition, and there are now often four ridden show classes.

A breakthrough in mixed classes was made in 1977 when Boffin of Transy, a black gelding bred by Mr Dougal Dick and ridden by his daughter Sarah, startled everyone at the Ponies of Britain Summer Show by not only coming fourth in the Child's First Pony class but also winning the Mountain and Moorland Small Breeds Handy Hunter; he was the only competitor to go clear over a course of jumps up to 3ft high and with a 4ft spread. Boffin and Sarah also jumped clear in the Handy Hunter championship next day against the large Mountain and Moorland ponies, over an even bigger course of jumps. An anonymous contributor to the Shetland magazine the next year rightly said: 'Well done Sarah, well done Boffin, well done Dougal – the three of you did more for the good name of Shetlands in twenty-four hours than many of us have done in as many years.'

85

THE NAN FRENCH MEMORIAL TROPHY

The Shetland Pony Stud-Book Society had by this time realised that ponies doing something useful should be encouraged as a good advertisement for the breed. The Nan French Memorial Trophy was donated in 1974 by Mr and Mrs Swannack in memory of Miss French, who had been a breeder of riding-and-driving Shetlands for many years and a leading exhibitor of ponies in harness (*see* Chapter 8). The Trophy was to be awarded to the exhibitor gaining the most points in ridden and driven classes throughout the year. In the first year that the award was given, it was clear that the system was tending to favour driving ponies: the winner was Mrs Rae whose stallion Hannibal of Hinton was shown under saddle but had gained most of his points in harness. The next year the award was given to individual ponies rather than exhibitors. Again the driving ponies predominated, with first, second and equal-third placings, but a ridden-only pony was fourth: Mrs Swinscow's skewbald mare Honey. In 1977 the top scorers were again the driving ponies, and the riding fraternity naturally felt disillusioned; this was one of the causes of the dwindling support for the Nan French Trophy at that time.

THE NPS CHAMPIONSHIPS

Things soon looked up. By the late 1970s a number of major shows ran ridden classes for Shetlands, often both Leading Rein and First Ridden. Places as far apart as Liskeard and Penrith had ridden Shetland classes at local shows, and there were also the new Shetland-only shows starting up. In 1979 the National Pony Society Ridden Mountain and Moorland Championship started up. The final is held at Olympia in December, and there are qualifying rounds at major shows round the country during the summer, including one qualifying class for each breed at its breed show. Competitors get a subsidy to help them attend the breed show qualifier.

Shetlands have done reasonably well at Olympia, considering that most Mountain and Moorland judges are still not used to thinking of a Shetland as a 'real' riding pony to be compared to a Connemara or a Welsh. In 1984, a great year for Shetlands, two ponies went to Olympia to represent the breed: Mrs House's black

Fig 47   Bincombe Pearl, ridden by Fleur Buchanan.

mare Bincombe Pearl and the Broothom Pony Stud's roan gelding
Clothie Eswick. Both performed extremely well, and it was thoroughly well deserved that Bincombe Pearl, ridden by Fleur Buchanan, was chosen to stand reserve champion (to a Connemara). The
feat was repeated in 1986, when Mrs Hampton's Bard of Transy,
ridden by March Rogers, also came in reserve champion. This pair
was again in the ribbons in the 1987 championship, finishing in
fourth place. Bard was the only small-breed pony in the final
line-up.

   More recently the National Pony Society has started up a similar
championship for Mountain and Moorland Working Hunter Ponies.
This includes jumping, with no concessions to the Shetlands' small
size, as well as the performance and conformation required for the
Ridden championship. Several Shetlands have qualified for the
finals, notably from the stables of Mrs Renwick, Mrs Hampton and
Mrs Webb, the doyennes of Shetland riding in the south. Another
national championship is the Ponies UK Mountain and Moorland,

Fig 48   A Leading Rein class in progress. The judge is Guy Hurst.

which is divided into Working, Ridden, and Leading Rein sections. Shetlands regularly qualify for all of these, and do especially well in the Leading Rein (Chatsworth Belle ridden by Walter Rogers was reserve champion in 1986). Perhaps Shetlands in the other classes suffer from a misconception about the size of the rider: a child of twelve or thirteen can look a bit underhorsed on a Shetland although he or she is certainly not too heavy for it. Yet there seems to be a prejudice against this while adults riding Dartmoors, for instance, are perfectly accepted.

A remarkable triumph for ridden Shetlands took place in May 1989, when Mrs Renwick entered four of the ponies who were doing the Grand National at the Royal Windsor Horse Show in the Pony Pairs class. The show secretary telephoned Mrs Renwick to say that it would not be appropriate to enter Shetlands for this class as they would be up against *'real* show ponies' of up to 15 hands, so would she like to withdraw the entries. The entries were not withdrawn, and two pairs of Shetlands (one black, one grey) went into the ring – to finish first and second!

At one time, quite a number of girls were to be seen riding Shetlands side-saddle. At the last of the Newbury Racecourse shows, there were five of them, but since then they have virtually disappeared. It is very difficult now to find a side-saddle that will fit a Shetland (though there must have been hundreds of them at one time, when all girls rode that way). One or two girls are taking up this charming style again, but they tend not to ride side-saddle for

Fig 49   The Pony Pairs class at the Royal Windsor Show 1989:
the winners were Riccalton Trampas (rider Carla Salmon) and
Ulverscroft Ebeneza (Nicola Dowell), with runners-up Brindle
Miranda (Jane Holden) and Ulverscroft Carisma (Stephanie
Branston). (Photo by Prints for Pleasure.)

major competitions, as there is a chance that judges will look upon it
as a gimmick and therefore not put a side-saddle rider at the top of
the line. It is not impossible that if enough saddles could be found
and enough girls taught to ride that way, there could be a separate
side-saddle class, perhaps at the Society's show. What a beautiful
sight it would be.

THE PERFORMANCE AWARDS

The reputation of Shetlands has never been better, and this is due
not only to the performance of the star ponies that go to Olympia
but also to the many who compete at a very high standard in ridden
classes all over the country. This is reflected in the new Performance
Awards scheme, which was started by Mrs Leivers (now Mrs
Renwick) in 1980 as a successor to the Nan French Trophy. The
ridden performance awards were separate from the start from the
driven ones. In the first year there were trophies for performance in
Leading Rein, in First Ridden, and in Gymkhana classes, as well as

Fig 50   One of the very few side-saddle Shetland riders: Victoria Joyce (aged 8), on Highwood Moonlight.

an overall champion. The overall champion was Mrs Bassett's skew-bald gelding Downlands Thorn, ridden by Simon Humphries. This competition was found to be such a success that in its second year it doubled its number of classes to six: Ridden, Leading Rein, Working Pony, Handy Pony, Best Pony of the Year and Best Rider of the Year. Doubling the number of riding classes again to twelve in 1982, the Performance Scheme went from strength to strength, and now consists of some thirty separate awards covering every conceivable activity that Shetlands can take part in under saddle – showing of every sort, dressage, Pony Club, hunting, Riding for the Disabled.

DRESSAGE

Shetlands are not often thought of as possible contenders at dressage, but perhaps that is because children young enough to be mounted on a Shetland are not often good enough riders to tackle a dressage test. But now that many young riders are learning to show Shetlands in the ring to the highest standard, dressage is becoming part of the Shetland repertoire. The pioneer in this direction was Cordelia Ayres who, at the age of twelve, rode Boxleaze Stud's mare Boxleaze Carona into first place in the Junior Prix Caprilli at the Bath Riding Club. This led to her being selected to represent the club the next year (1986) in the Riding Clubs Junior National Championships. Her team won its zone competition and went on to the finals at Stoneleigh where Cordelia and Carona were awarded third individual prize and the team came fifth.

Dressage is of course part of the agenda for combined training events, and for these Shetlands seem at first sight even less likely candidates than for pure dressage. Yet one-day events for Shetlands have been held successfully for several years on the Islands, and there was one at Chatsworth in 1983 which even included a section for Leading Rein in which ponies, riders and leaders had to get round a cross-country course of four jumps.

CAN SHETLANDS JUMP?

Leading-rein jumping is perhaps the one area in which there is room for doubt about whether the present competitions are good for

91

Fig 51 Shetlands can jump: Lakeland Dew ridden by Anna
Staveley clears timber in perfect style. (Photo by Carol Gilson.)

Fig 52 Leading-rein jumping: how it should be done. Jenny Webb on Riccalton Trampas.

Fig 53 A prolific winner in ridden classes: Bard of Transy, bred by D.W.H. Dick, owned by Mrs V. Hampton, and ridden by Charlotte Rogers.

the Shetland's reputation. In any of these classes there will be several well-schooled ponies that will follow the leader over anything, jumping fluently. But there will also be some ponies who have obviously not been taught to jump properly; it is not an edifying sight to see one of these sticking its feet down in front of an innocuous little pair of crossed poles. Still less edifying is the sight when this pony suddenly decides that it will jump after all – it leaps off all four legs at once like a goat, and more probably than not unseats its unfortunate small rider.

Shetlands are as capable of jumping as any other pony, and do well in relation to their size. The size of the fences for the NPS and Ponies UK Championships is 2ft 3in high with a 2ft spread, and they are built to look imposing. This is pretty high for an average Shetland, but the athletic types who go in for the Working Hunter Pony championships can go higher and wider with ease.

Fig 54   Endurance pony: Seva Marmaduke is off hunting this time, ridden by Tania Davies.

Fig 55   At the end of the day there is always the gymkhana:
Emma Stevens on Victory of Catchpool and Christopher
Stevens on Shadow of Catchpool.

LONG-DISTANCE RIDING

The famous Shetland stamina – the ability to 'carry a man or woman twenty miles a day' – stands the ponies in good stead when they take part in long-distance rides. Not very many Shetlands go in for these, perhaps because people are worried that they will not be able to keep up with the other ponies and horses. In Wales, Seva Marmaduke ridden by Rebecca Davies made a great name for himself with the Welsh branch of the Endurance Horse and Pony Society. Far from being in danger of getting left behind, Marmaduke would often lead the way through rivers and up and down steep places. Shetland ponies must have their own folk-memories of the Islands.

8

Shetlands as Driving Ponies

Shetlands began to be famous and fashionable for driving in the Victorian age, as we saw in Chapter 3. As soon as breeding began to be taken seriously, at the end of the nineteenth century, there were show classes for Shetlands in harness as well as in hand. The Ladies Hope were very keen drivers, and established a great reputation particularly with their remarkable mare Hoplemuroma, a roan standing only 35½in. In 1920 she won a trotting handicap for ponies up to 14 hands high, carrying a four-stone boy; but she was also capable of great speeds with an adult in the trap, being credited with covering four miles in 16 minutes, a speed of 15 miles per hour.[1]

In the show ring, Shetlands were usually driven to a show waggon or some other very light vehicle, the idea being that these gave the pony a better chance to show its paces than a conventional vehicle would. Also in the interests of lightness, only ladies or boys would drive (with unselfconscious class distinction the rules for the International Horse Show of 1920 state: 'To be driven by ladies or boys under sixteen – stable boys barred').[2] These classes were lively affairs, with the ponies trotting at top speed to the accompaniment of a brass band playing suitable music – usually the Posthorn Gallop or the William Tell Overture. Judging was solely on the pony's performance. The same people who were winning in the in-hand showing also exhibited their ponies in harness classes, though perhaps a slightly leggier pony would be more likely to do well in the latter.

Shetlands in harness were also part of everyday life right up to the war. Cars were coming in, of course, but they were still expensive and tricky compared to a reliable pony. Countless Shetlands did short-haul transport jobs in the country such as fetching passengers from the station. After the war things had changed for harness ponies. In towns there were hardly any horse-drawn vehicles left except the milk-floats, and in the country cars had replaced horses and ponies. Vehicles and harness were burnt or left to rot. In the show ring there were still classes for private driving, trade turnouts and hackneys, but on a scale much reduced from what there had been before the war.

SHOW DRIVING REVIVED

In 1962 a few enthusiasts got together to start up Shetland show driving again. The prime movers were Miss Nan French, Lady Joan Gore-Langton, and Mrs Shirley Swannack, all of whom had taken part in the Shetland driving classes before the war. They put on a display at Brighton in 1962, and were able to persuade four shows to hold classes in the following year. As in former days, Shetlands were to be driven to show waggons only (or some other similar light vehicle), as either pairs or singles; judging was to be on performance only; the one thing that was different was that music was not provided. These classes were quite well supported, with at least half a dozen turnouts usually forward.

Fig 56   A show waggon class: Mrs Swannack driving her home-bred Midnight of Woodbury heads the line-up. Lady Joan Gore-Langton driving a light-coloured pony stands third.

After a year or two some entries were Shetlands driven to tradi-
tional vehicles – rallis, governess cars, etc. – so that the class would be
half-way towards a private driving one. Judges and exhibitors were
confused as to what was wanted, and support for Shetland classes
fell away rapidly as a result. In 1968 Mrs Swannack pleaded for a
return to the original idea:

> Shetland driving is dying for lack of support. When the sport was
> revived in 1962, by a few enthusiasts, it was intended that if possible
> the classes should be run the same as before the war. That is, most
> ponies in show waggons or sulkies, although other vehicles could be
> used, and the class to be judged *entirely* on the performance of the
> pony. Providing everything was clean and tidy, nobody cared if the
> harness was old and the vehicle needed painting or the driver a new
> hat! It was the ponies' condition, movement and general performance
> that mattered.
>
> Now, no one seems to know what they want. Most of us used
> show waggons at first and the cry promptly came that 'only fat black
> stallions in show waggons ever win. No one with a nice little vehicle
> stands a chance.' So (reluctantly on my part), most of us searched for
> nice little vehicles and made endless extra work and expenses for
> ourselves. Now I have recently heard it said that the standard of the
> turnouts is too high and so it is no good competing. I must say I am
> quite baffled.
>
> In my opinion, most vehicles used for Shetlands are too big and
> heavy, making it impossible for the ponies to move freely and give
> the same sparkling performance that they can be trained to provide in
> a show waggon or a very light vehicle. Besides, it is all so much more
> fun and so much fairer if all competitors have similar types of
> vehicles.[3]

These very sensible words went unheeded. Show waggons disappeared from the ring, and one show after another dropped its
Shetlands-only harness class. However, there was still the class at
the Newbury Racecourse Shetland show, and also one at the British
Driving Society's annual show at Smith's Lawn, Windsor.

In fact although the number of turnouts competing was not large
the standard was extremely high, and it was not long before Shet-
lands came high up the line or even at the top in Open Private
Driving classes at major shows. In the mid 1970s the public image of
Shetlands got a boost from the driving exploits of several ponies.
One of them was Mrs Rae's Hannibal of Hinton, who won the
Under-13.2 Ride and Drive at the British Driving Society show in

Fig 57   The Staveley family's pair Lakeland Lightning and
Ulverscroft Cameron.

Fig 58   The Woods family's pair Tawna Golant and Tawna
Gwithian.

1976 and went on to be reserve champion of the Ride and Drive section; this 36in black stallion was also extremely successful in in-hand showing. In the following year the Staveley family took first prize at the Royal Show in the Open Pairs with Lakeland Lightning and Ulverscroft Cameron, and were also overall reserve champions of the driving classes (Lightning, a 38½in bay stallion, was another prolific winner in-hand). This pair had also won the Concours d'Elegance at the North West Driving Championships the previous year, which disposed of any prejudices that small ponies may be able to pull but they cannot look elegant while they do it.

COMPETITION DRIVING

At about the same time Shetlands began to compete in combined driving events. These are held under the rules of the FEI (Fédération Equestre Internationale), and consist of presentation, dressage, marathon (about fifteen miles, some on roads and some across country, with hazards including water), and obstacle driving. One of the pioneers of using Shetlands in these competitions was Mr David Morgan-Davies; his view was that 'The Shetland pony is a perfect horse (pony) for Combined Driving except for one small problem; it is small'.[4] He advocated driving Shetlands in pairs or teams, and recommended ponies as near as possible to the full height of 42in. He was extremely successful with his Shetlands; at the Lowther Trials in 1974 he came first with his team (wheelers his own roans Norge of Belmont and Treasure of Belmont, leaders Mrs King's blacks, Ickworth Avenger and Ickworth Bismarck, all stallions) in spite of breaking the pole half-way round an exceptionally tough marathon course. He was also second in the pairs.

The Staveleys were also very successful in combined driving. On their very first outing with Lightning and Cameron as a pair, at Beamish in 1976, they won the pairs. The following year they added two more ponies to make a team, and came second at Holker Hall and at the Scottish Driving Trials, among other successes. Many other drivers have followed, competing in FEI trials with teams, pairs, and even tandems.

In spite of the problem of their small size, Shetlands can compete in combined driving in single harness. The difficulty is that FEI rules specify a minimum weight for the vehicle, and also insist that two people are carried. This is disproportionately hard on the Shetlands,

Fig 59 Mrs Carlisle competing at Castle Howard with her
ponies Eastlands Sunstroke and Tibthorpe Peneleway. (Photo
by Anne Grossick.)

but since the groom is essential for safety on the marathon course it
cannot be helped. A really strong Shetland, almost certainly a
stallion, can manage it. Mrs Staveley, who has driven Lightning as a
single, feels that public opinion is holding people back from attempt-
ing to compete with Shetlands, as there is a mistaken belief that it is
cruel. This is a pity, because there are many keen drivers who only
have one pony who would enjoy FEI driving.

Shetland ponies have an absolute genius for the type of driving
that involves accuracy, and they are nearly unbeatable at obstacle
and scurry driving. In these competitions, vehicles have to be
driven at speed round twisting courses marked out with cones and
there are penalties for knocking down any of the obstacles. The
scurry is always against the clock, and is an exciting competition to
watch, with pairs of ponies galloping flat out from one obstacle to
the next. A popular attraction at the Horse of the Year Show for
many years, where Mrs Dick's Shetlands Peanut and Pavlov seemed
to have thousands of fans, the scurry is still part of the fun at many
of the big shows, and the winners are nearly always Shetlands.

Fig 60 Mrs Brooker's Star of North Dale, driven by Geoffrey
Scott with groom Graham Leith.

SUPPORT FROM THE SOCIETY

The Shetland Pony Stud-Book Society has supported the revival of driving as much as it can. The annual award in memory of Miss Nan French, mentioned in Chapter 7, was for performance in driving as well as ridden classes. In fact, the winners of the Trophy for the first three years were the leading names in driving: Hannibal of Hinton won in 1974 and 1975, and just lost his title to Lakeland Lightning in 1976.

The Performance Awards were reorganised on a larger scale by Mrs Leivers (now Mrs Renwick) in 1980 with a separate section for driving run by Mrs Gough. The first winner of the new-style award's driven section was Lakeland Lightning, who was also overall champion. There was also a trophy for the best junior whip; not many competed for this in the early days, but more are doing so now, so that one can expect a skilled new generation of drivers to replace the old hands in due course. The Performance Awards were very well supported from the start, and have become more and more diversified each year. The driving scheme is now organised separately from the Ridden awards, under the management of Mrs

Fig 61   Mrs Brooker driving her pair Clothie Gloup and Clothie Gluss.

Fig 62   The author with her own-design exercise cart, with
Lockinge Shelley.

Gardner, and there are six sections: single turnout, multiple turn-out, rallies and picnic drivers, junior whip, working pony, and Riding for the Disabled driving (*see* Chapter 9). It is perhaps a pity that there are not separate show classes, at the Society's show and at other Shetland-only shows, for Shetland driven to exercise vehicles. True, there are often special prizes for the highest-placed pony in an exercise vehicle in the driven Shetland class, but a separate class for them would bring back Mrs Swannack's ideal of a class in which judging was solely on the pony's performance and in which the amount of money spent in the turnout would be irrelevant. Points won in these classes could go towards a separate section in the Performance Awards.

It was a very good idea to include non-competitive driving in the Society's Performance Awards, as that is what the vast majority of Shetlands in harness now are used for. Up and down the country there are very many outgrown children's ponies being driven just for fun, or perhaps retired show or driving ponies keeping their hands in just for fun with BDS rallies or even more informal events. There are certainly a good number of them in the New Forest, ideal driving country. There is a group of Shetland enthusiasts – Mrs Parsons, Mrs Handcock and Mrs Serjeant in particular – who used to meet regularly for all-Shetland picnic drives. They even went for a five-day tour once, putting themselves and the ponies up at various pubs on their route round the Forest and covering eighty miles almost all on forest tracks.

SHETLANDS FOR FARM WORK

Some owners have used their Shetlands for work round the farm or garden. The oil crisis in the early 1970s prompted some people to put their pony in a trap to go and do the shopping or to take the children to school. On a more serious level, one smallholder,

Fig 63   Part of a picnic drive in the New Forest.

Fig 64   Mrs Braithwaite's
Beacon Andrew taking
hay to the sheep.

Dr Wright, used a Shetland mare for all work on her land: ploughing, harrowing and sowing.[6] It was very heavy work for one pony, so now she uses a pair (her three ponies are all mares, who take a break from the land to breed a foal from time to time). Shetlands like work, and even if you could actually do the job some other way, you are doing the pony a favour if you let it make itself useful by carting the dead leaves off the garden or taking the hay up to the other ponies in the top field.

9

'All in a Good Cause . . .'

Even though they cannot fully understand what they are doing, it is no surprise to find the generous-natured Shetland ponies engaged in good works of various kinds. It may be as simple a thing as giving rides at the village fête to raise funds for the church tower restoration, or the scanner for the local hospital, or cancer research. Many Shetland owners must have memories of long afternoons plodding up and down the vicarage lawn in either sweltering heat or penetrating drizzle, endlessly altering stirrups and placing pudgy hands the right way round on the reins; our patience gives out long before the pony's does.

Fig 65   Garden party duty: Mrs Osborne's Jerry collecting for the RDA.

Fig 66   A display drive of RDA ponies at Kenilworth. The Shetlands are Mrs Fox's Sugar Plum of Inkpen and Joanna of Inkpen. (Photo by Trevor Meeks.)

RIDING FOR THE DISABLED

At a more organised level, Shetland ponies have been staunch supporters of the Riding for the Disabled Association right from the beginning. The Association, a registered charity, started life in 1969, founded by a group of horsemen and medical people who saw that riding could provide not just recreation but a breakthrough in independence and self-esteem for handicapped people. It was a brilliant idea, and the growth of the RDA shows how much it was welcomed by disabled: in 1970 there were 2,400 riders, and by 1988 there were nearly 24,000. No one has to travel far to get their riding, as the RDA is organised on a regional basis and has nearly 700 local groups holding sessions once a week. All the riders are referred to the RDA by their doctors and in fact the majority are so severely handicapped that they are already receiving care or training at a special school or hospital. In the early days, adults were not usually taken on as riders, but now one-third of RDA pupils are adults (this is partly because of the introduction of driving as well as riding). Over the years there has been a great increase in the proportion of mentally rather than physically handicapped riders, and they are now in the majority at 65 per cent. They seem to benefit not just from the relationship with the pony that they ride or drive but also from the friendships that they form with the voluntary helpers.

Shetland ponies are particularly well suited to the work of the RDA. Their small size is a great advantage: a helper can walk beside the pony with an arm comfortably round the rider, or a person in a wheelchair can reach all over the pony, to touch it and learn its points, to groom it and pick out its feet. The patience required by the pony is immense, for it can take a handicapped child a very long time indeed to accomplish even the simplest task. Picture the ponies standing on three legs as still as statues while the riders struggle with getting the hoof-pick anywhere near the hoof. In some RDA groups Shetlands specialise in this side of things, being the guinea-pigs for grooming and tacking up for all the riders, while bigger ponies do the actual riding lessons. Shetlands are used only for the younger riders. They could be up to the weight of an adult, but it is difficult for anyone to ride properly if their feet are nearly touching

Fig 67   The perfect size: Kirkstall Butterfly with disabled rider and helpers.

Fig 68   Robin's Brae Irvine ridden by Kevin Godwin gained
fifth prize in the Open Mountain and Moorland class at
Plymouth Horse Show.

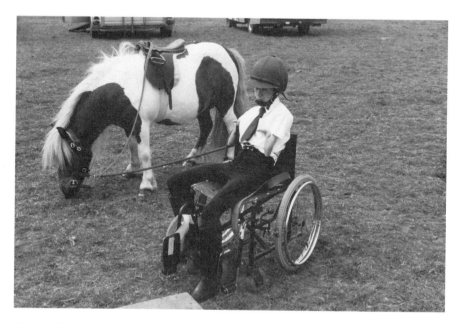

Fig 69   The same pair relaxing.

the ground, and even more so for a disabled person. This meant that Shetlands in the RDA were pensioned off, so to speak, if there happened to be no young rider in the group.

DRIVING FOR THE DISABLED

Then Driving for the Disabled started up. It was an obvious extension of the RDA: many people whose disability prevented them from riding a horse or pony could get the same benefits from driving it. A start was made in 1975, with one specially-built vehicle with a ramp so that a person in a wheelchair could get in and sit alongside an able-bodied driver. Once again, the scheme was a great success: the seriously handicapped drivers found an exhilarating sense of freedom in being able to go with their pony and vehicle exactly where any able-bodied driver would go. Some of the drivers were people who had already been riding with the RDA but had had to give up when their disabilities got worse; some had never been able

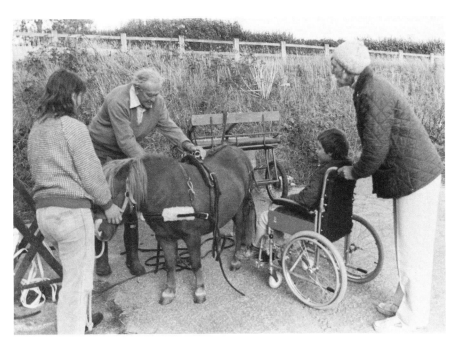

Fig 70   Merrymead Teasle working with the Diptford RDA Group. (Photo by Wyn Hughes.)

111

to ride at all. Since then driving has become a significant part of the RDA's activities, with nearly 600 drivers in 100 local groups.

Once again, Shetland ponies have come to the fore. An ordinary exercise cart is often easy enough to get into for a disabled driver to be able to use it with only minor modifications, e.g. extra arm-rails, attachments for a safety-belt, or else a specially adapted vehicle can be built at a more economical cost than for a larger pony. The back of the vehicle lets down to form a ramp for a wheelchair. A Shetland is so low that the disabled driver can reach to help with harnessing up or even with putting-to, slipping in the lightweight shaft into the tug.

Safety rules are strict, and include the absolutely unbreakable rule that an able-bodied whip is always in the vehicle with the disabled driver, with a second pair of reins (rather like a dual-control driving-school car, and similarly not often needed). Shetland ponies find no problem at all with the weight. They are the strongest of all horses and ponies in proportion to their weight (as has been proved time and again in draught contests), and they have no difficulty with

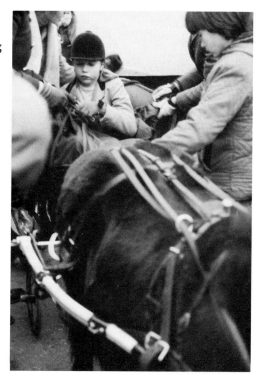

Fig 71 Olivia Graham needs a special grip to hold the reins for driving (the pony is Mrs Fox's Sugar Plum of Inkpen).

Fig 72 The Best Disabled Driver class at the British Driving
Society's Smith's Lawn show.

pulling two adults, even up and down hills or across country. It
goes without saying that their unflappable temperament is another
great asset. They will stand rock-like while crutches or wheelchairs
or whatever are organised and everybody is safely settled in. They
also seem to know that best behaviour is called for when the driver
is disabled. Mrs Swinscow reports that her pony Robin's Brae Irvine
(Robin to his friends) is a mad-keen competitor in the cone-driving
when she is at the reins, whizzing round like a wasp, but when his
disabled driver takes over he will solemnly walk round exactly the
same course. He seems to know that he must be quiet at this time.
Robin is a 38in skewbald gelding, bred in the Islands, and his
photograph is in the latest promotion leaflet of the RDA's driving
section. One of his disabled drivers, Susan Baldie, did driving as her
sport for her Silver Duke of Edinburgh award, which was presented
to her by Prince Edward in 1988.

Fig 73   Susie Baldie on her way to collect her Duke of
Edinburgh Award from Prince Edward (Mrs Swinscow co-
driving her Robin's Brae Irvine).

THE RDA CHAMPIONSHIP

Ten years ago the RDA began its national championship, sponsored
by Lloyds Bank. It is a competition for the horses and ponies who
help regularly with RDA work; there are regional qualifying competitions at local shows, then semi-finals at Epsom in October prior
to the finals which were at the Horse of the Year Show at Wembley
up to 1988. Looks are nothing to do with it; knowing the job is. The
ponies have to prove their general manageability, doing such things
as standing quietly while tied up for several minutes, loading and
unloading, being led in and out of narrow entrances, etc. For safety
reasons, disabled riders do not take part in the actual competition,
but they are 'represented' by helpers thumping and bumping into
the ponies' sides while they are carrying weights. The ponies also
do ridden tests, with an inexperienced small child rider and then

114

Fig 74   Mrs Carter's Blue Chintz of Annwood.

with a lightweight adult who will really try their paces, including jumping. The most popular part of the competition from the specta-tors' point of view is the 'noise and hazard test' in which the pony must face all sorts of likely and unlikely hazards, such as suddenly-opening umbrellas or falling boxes, or having to walk under a mock washing line or over a sheet of polythene. Shetlands are notably stoical about such things. In the second year that the competition was run, Mrs Carter's Blue Chintz of Annwood (a very versatile and accomplished pony, winner of many performance awards) brought honour to the breed by coming in Reserve Champion at Wembley. He was Reserve again in the following two years, and was the Champion the year after (1983). Robin's Brae Irvine has also done well in the Lloyd's Championship, coming seventh in 1988 out of more than 300 competitors.

RDA work is one of the categories in the annual Performance Awards run by the Shetland Pony Stud-Book Society. There are separate awards for RDA riding and RDA driving, calculated on a points basis; there are points given for each session at an RDA

115

Fig 75   Mrs Adorian's Toyhorse Tomboy and Toyhorse Little
Fiend collecting in London for the Wishing Well Appeal.

centre, and a separate section in which points are given for ponies
that compete in the qualifiers for the Lloyd's championship. Shetland ponies also do their bit for the RDA by taking part in fund-
raising activities such as sponsored rides or drives, and the RDA is
one of the favourite charities for donations from shows, notably the
Hermitage Show held every September. Some ponies that help out
with the rides are also good at passing round the hat.

PETS FOR HANDICAPPED CHILDREN

The instinct that Shetlands have for behaving gently with disabled
riders or drivers is brought out even more when the patient is too
disabled to do anything more than be the pony's friend. Mrs
Adorian, who breeds miniature Shetlands, is often approached by
parents of severely handicapped children who feel that they would
benefit from having a pony in their life, even if there could be no
hope of their riding it. One of her ponies went to a small child semi-
paralysed by poliomyelitis; the little boy had previously been unable

to go out for walks, and still could not walk himself, but the pleasure of being wheeled out alongside this pony transformed his life. Another tiny pony (only 27in high) became the companion of a severely brain-damaged nine-year-old girl, and taught her to walk. The child made such progress that within a year she was well enough to learn to ride, and a larger Shetland was bought from Mrs Adorian to teach her. Alas, after only a few months the poor girl suffered a further cerebral infection, and relapsed totally. Once again she was unable to walk, and her companion the tiny pony was the only hope of getting her on her feet again, which she eventually did. They are still together now, with the girl in her late teens and still, unfortunately, severely handicapped. However, she still enjoys her daily walk with her first pony.

Mrs Adorian was a staunch supporter of Great Ormond Street Children's Hospital's Wishing Well Appeal in 1987/88. She helped to organise a marathon drive from Billingshurst near her farm in Sussex right to the hospital in North London, a distance of about fifty-five miles. Half a dozen turnouts took part, mostly big ponies or horses (including a team of Cleveland Bays), but also two Shetland ponies: a standard-sized black mare and Mrs Adorian's miniature stallion Toyhorse Tomboy. The route went past the Chessington 'World of Adventures', where a fund-raising stop was made by Tomboy and his stable-mate Little Fiend. The pair of them raised £700 for the Wishing Well in the one day, and the whole marathon made nearly £5,000. Mrs Adorian also holds Open Days in aid of Great Ormond Street. Her farm has been adapted so that people in wheelchairs can go everywhere, and this has contributed to the success of the Open Days, which had 2,000 visitors in 1987 and about 3,500 in 1988.

THE GRAND NATIONAL

Great Ormond Street Children's Hospital is very much part of the Shetland world, as it is the charity for which the famous Grand National is run. One cannot imagine what all the sporty Shetlands did with themselves before they were allowed to show off in public by galloping full-tilt round the ring. The Grand National was started in 1982, from an idea that came partly from the Shetland fraternity themselves and partly from Raymond Brooks-Ward's British Equestrian Promotions. In its first year Sue Ryder Homes received the

Fig 76   The Grand National.

proceeds, but since 1983 the money has gone to Great Ormond Street, the charity chosen by Mrs Renwick, who has organised the Grand National right from the beginning. The Grand National is a race – a *real* race with the ponies galloping flat out. There are five fences and the ponies go round the course two and a half times, so they jump twelve times. The length of the course varies from one show to another. In the first year the competitors were chosen by Mrs Renwick from among the successful ponies in the Performance Awards (*see* Chapter 7), but after that there was a system of qualifying races held at major shows, e.g. Three Counties, the Royal Highland, the South of England, the Royal Welsh, to select the ten ponies to go and run in the final Grand National at Olympia in December.

In order to compete in the qualifiers, both pony and rider must have been registered with the Performance Awards scheme for the preceding year. The reason for this rule is safety; the Grand National is tough, and only experienced ponies and riders can cope with it. Riders have to be between nine and thirteen years old. Ponies have to be at least five years old to qualify, but most are quite a bit older. Handsome is as handsome does, and looks are not necessarily required, but it is noticeable that good ponies – well-made and good movers – do best. Several of the ponies qualifying for the Olympia Grand National have also qualified for the National Pony Society Mountain and Moorland Ridden Championship or Working Hunter Championship.

One of the best-known competitors in the Grand National is Mrs Stevens's Vandal of Catchpool. At only 36in he is one of the smallest runners, but he makes up for his small size by his outstanding cussedness. On one of his visits to Olympia he was ridden into the ring by a steward who soon found himself sitting in the sawdust. Vandal, terribly pleased with himself, held up proceedings for a good ten minutes while he charged round the arena refusing to be caught. In spite of, or perhaps because of, this escapade his picture was chosen to advertise the 1989 Grand National.

The sponsors (Larch-Lap International until 1986, Volvo since then) put up the cash for the expenses of running the Grand

Fig 77   The start of a 'fun' Grand National at the South Wales Shetland Show, 1988.

Fig 78   Vandal of Catchpool is about to demonstrate that
he will not be made a fool of by anybody.

Fig 79 Ponies and riders from the Grand National team
appeared on Blue Peter. (Photo by courtesy of BBC TV.)

National at Olympia and at the qualifiers, so that every pound the
public puts in can go directly to Great Ormond Street. Money is
raised by appealing to the British fantasy of owning a racehorse:
'ownership' of the pony for a day is sold, so that all the supporters
watching the race can cheer for their very 'own' pony. Mrs Renwick
also organises displays of the Grand National ponies at major
equestrian events such as the Royal Windsor Horse Show and the
Greater London Horse Show in Hyde Park, which bring in more
money in donations.

At the end of the season the children who have ridden in the
Grand National go on a visit to the hospital, taking with them a real
live pony that goes with them into the wards and behaves impecc-
ably. In the six years from 1983 to 1988 Mrs Renwick and her helpers
have raised over £100,000 for the hospital. The money is spent on
specific items of medical equipment, and each item is marked with a
commemorative plaque to record that it was bought through the
efforts of those dedicated children and ponies.

10

The Shetland Islands

Perhaps the main difference between the Shetland pony scene in the Shetland Islands and elsewhere is that on the Islands the breeders are heirs of a tradition. In Shetland, if you are interested in ponies or horses, it will be Shetland ponies that you have. Indeed, the word 'horse' in Shetland speech means, in the first place, a Shetland pony. This is very much in contrast to the position in Scotland, England, Holland, etc. where Shetland ponies are taken up as a hobby and are chosen from among the various breeds of ponies and horses available.

This sense of tradition among Island breeders is without any parallel in the horse world. Many of the breeders today have their great-grandfathers' names in the membership list in the first volume of the Stud Book, and no doubt the family tradition goes on for centuries before that. A typical example is the Jamieson family of Walls, in the western part of the Mainland, a stronghold of pony-breeding as far back as records go. Mr Tom Jamieson kindly lent me a photograph of his family taken in about 1918; there is of course a Shetland pony in the picture, and it is of course at work. (The cows are Shetland cows, now a very rare breed in danger of dying out; only a handful of pure-bred Shetland cows are still kept on the Islands, and they have never attracted much of a following else-where, unlike the ponies.)

WORK ON THE CROFTS

Many people in Shetland can describe from their own memory what it was like when 'horses' (Shetland ponies) were the only power on the crofts. Mr Bobby Laurenson of Bridge of Walls recounted how as a boy he would be given charge of a string of ponies to carry the peats down from the hill to the house. He remembered that this work was usually done by geldings, as the mares' more important

122

Fig 80   The Jamieson family of Summerside, Walls, Shetland,
in about 1918. The couple on the extreme right are the
grandparents of Mr Tom Jamieson of Lochside, Walls.

occupation was breeding foals. (Similarly, taking charge of the
ponies would be a job for boys, leaving women to get on with the
many domestic and dairy chores and men to get on with men's
work.) Up on the hill where the peat had been dug, makeshift tables
would be put up in pairs to form stalls so that the ponies could be
more easily loaded up. The business of carrying the peats down
took weeks, day in, day out, during the hottest part of the year.
Each boy would lead a string of six or seven ponies, the ponies
being roped together, one behind the other. Down at the croft one
of the men would build the peats up into a stack, with the peats
sloping outwards so that the rain would run off; this was quite an
art, and not everyone could achieve a good stack.

The ponies at that time were of a good size, about 40in high
according to Mr Laurenson (as the pony in the Jamieson picture
seems to be). He recalled that a pair of ponies that size were able to
draw a plough (this is in contrast to the nineteenth-century accounts
– *see* Chapter 2). The plough was of the type known as an American
plough, which was small and had a wooden beam. Progress was
slow, but the area on a croft that had to be ploughed was usually
only between one and two acres. Ponies were also used for the
somewhat lighter work of drawing the harrow, which had wooden

Fig 81 Merrylegs, owned by Mrs Hall, drawing a load of hay in a net. This mare, 42in high, is of a type not often seen in the Islands now. She was not replaced on the croft by a tractor until 1974, when she was fifteen years old, and she continued to do odd jobs for the following fifteen years.

tines. Harness for both ploughing and harrowing consisted of collar and hames, with a band or pad on the back to support the chains by which the implement was pulled. Mr Laurenson can also remember that if a pony was not available a human would pull the harrow; he has done this himself, pulling on a rope over the back of the neck and under each arm like a satchel-strap. Ponies also drew carts to carry any loads around the croft: manure, hay, potatoes, etc.

The Shetland Islands are no place for luxuries. If crofters still keep ponies it is not for fun or for the work on the croft (now mechanised) but for sale, as part of the income of the croft. This is reflected in the fact that there are far fewer activities for Shetland ponies in their native islands than in the southern countries, where there are many Shetlands going hunting or competing in gymkhanas or being driven. Only a very few ponies in the Islands are involved in this sort of thing. (Among the few are the ponies owned and trained by Mrs Helen Thomson at Dunrossness, which visit England to compete every year and are regular winners in the Performance Awards.) By far the greater part of the population of Shetland ponies on the Islands is in breeding herds, consisting of ponies only halter-broken.

SELLING PONIES

Usually all the foals are sold each year, with very few ponies being retained for breeding or to be sold later as youngstock. The Shetland

Fig 82   A typical croft in the Shetland Islands. Only the area
enclosed in the wall would have been ploughed. This
abandoned croft is at Haroldswick, in the north of Unst.

breeders are faced with a difficult decision as to where to sell their
foals. The auctions held on the Islands are more convenient and the
transport costs are very low, but so are the prices. If foals are sent
down to Aberdeen the prices will be higher, but so will the transport
costs; the general opinion is that the journey to Aberdeen is not
worth the trouble. At Reading the prices are far better, and in recent
years have been spectacular, but with the cost of taking a lorry from
the Islands to Reading at not far short of £1000, there is still a
gamble. In 1986 the Shetland Island breeders got a subsidy of 75 per
cent from the Highlands and Islands Development Board towards
the expenses of sending their foals to 'the best market in Britain',
which is of course Reading. The subsidy continued over the next
two years, though it was reduced to 50 then 25 per cent of costs;
now the Shetlanders have to meet all the costs themselves. The
breeders agree that the journey to Reading has been well worth it, in

125

Fig 83   Clothie Eswick, one of Mrs Thomson's outstanding ridden ponies, competing at a gymkhana on Shetland.

Fig 84 The autumn sale at Lerwick some years ago.

Fig 85 The new saleroom building at Baltasound put up in
1989 with money raised by the Shetland breeders of Unst.

terms not only of cash but also prestige: Island foals have won the
show championship every time from 1986. Happily, this prestige is
now being reflected in rather higher prices at the northern sales, as
discriminating buyers take the trouble to travel up in search of
quality.

PONY BREEDERS OF SHETLAND ASSOCIATION

The Pony Breeders of Shetland Association is very active in keeping
up the standard of the ponies being bred, and organises two
schemes funded by the Stud-Book Society. First is the Shetland
Islands Premium Stallion Scheme, under which quality stallions are
loaned to run on the scattalds (this began in the 1950s – *see* Chapter
5). The members of the Association choose the stallions; colour is
considered very important, and is carefully selected to match the
needs of the mares on each particular scattald. There are seven
scattalds in the scheme: five on Unst, one in Walls, one in the south
Mainland. (There used to be far more scattald grazing on the
Islands, but more and more of the hill land is being fenced so now
the majority of ponies are kept and bred not on scattalds but in
fenced land ('parks') around the crofts.)

A herd on the scattald on Unst, the most northerly of the
Shetland Islands.

Mrs S. Wall's Goldan Chieftain, taking part in the Regent's
Park Parade.

Lakeland Lightning enjoying retirement.

The other scheme is the Premium Filly and Colt Scheme. This was started in 1983 to encourage breeders to keep back good youngsters for breeding stock. Fillies must be three years old, colts two, and they are inspected in early autumn by two panel judges to make sure they are of a good enough standard. They must be retained for two years and bred from in order for the breeder to keep the premium (£20 in 1989). This scheme was originally funded by a grant from the Horse Race Betting Levy Board.

A SMALLER TYPE OF PONY

The type of pony being bred on the Islands now is smaller than it was when croft work was the end in view. Nowadays 34in or under

Fig 86   Just one of the island-bred ponies doing well in the show ring in England: Mootie of Lochside, winner of the Normandykes Cup (bred by T.A.J. Jamieson and owned by Mrs Joseph).

Fig 87   Ponies in ideal conditions: The Smiths' Berry herd high on the hills above Scalloway.

ponies are very prominent, which is not surprising since these are the ones that fetch the money at the sales (*see* Chapter 12). Black ponies are in a minority, and broken-coloured ones, particularly skewbalds, are popular. Some breeders have brought in small broken-coloured stallions from England or Scotland to get this type established. Ponies upwards of 38in are a rarity, though there are a few breeders specialising in the old-fashioned type.

PROBLEMS ON THE ISLANDS

Apart from the problem of the sales, breeders in the Islands face quite a number of difficulties that southerners do not. One is the cost of foodstuffs. Hay is expensive even if it is locally grown, and nuts or corn can be anything up to three times the cost in the south, as they all have to be imported. There is no knacker in the islands, so that the only thing to be done when a pony dies is to send for a JCB and get a large hole dug. There are vets: just two of them for the whole of the Islands. And they are both based in Lerwick, on the Mainland, so breeders on any of the islands are dependent on the vet being able to catch a ferry. In the case of Unst, where there are many Shetland breeders, it is a matter of two different ferry crossings, so getting a vet in for an emergency is out of the question.

However, Island breeders have one enormous advantage to compensate for all these things: the terrain. There is no doubt that ponies kept on these windswept hills are in their ideal environment. They cannot help keeping fit as they cover the rocky ground looking for their food; they simply never get fat or footy.

11

Shetlands Round the World

The first ponies sold from the Shetland Islands to destinations outside the British Isles went to Holland or North Germany. This had probably been going on for as long as the foreign fishing fleets had been coming to the Islands; certainly it is recorded in 1633:

> They send to the Foreigners their Cod, Ling, and tusk, and Herring, and Sheaths; and the Oyle they make of the Fishes they take, and Butter, and their Horses, Cows and Sheep.[1]

But as noted in Chapter 4, this trade was very sporadic. Systematic exports did not occur until Victorian times.

AUSTRALIA

The earliest shipment of Shetlands exported to set up a stud abroad was probably the one that went to Australia in 1858. Mr Andrew Lyall of Western Victoria had gone to the Shetland Islands to buy a breeding herd for himself and one for his brother William.[2] He chose two stallions and nineteen mares, all of which made the long journey safely. More shipments were sent soon after, and by the 1870s there were reportedly several herds of a hundred ponies or more. A little later one of the leading enthusiasts was Colonel Thomas Small who called his farm 'Shetland Heights'; he had many Australian-bred ponies but also bought some more stock from the Shetland Islands in the 1890s.

The first ponies registered in the Shetland Pony Stud Book to go out to Australia were bought by Mrs MacLellan, the new owner of 'Shetland Heights', in 1911. In 1912 she imported a stallion bred by the Ladies Hope, Halcyon of Bodiam. This beautiful pony was the foundation sire of registered Shetlands in Australia; he was joined in the 1920s by stallions of Transy and Penniwells breeding.

The Australian Pony Stud Book was founded in 1931. This is still the book in which Shetlands in Australia are registered but there is now a Shetland Pony Owners and Breeders Society of Australia. The typical Australian Shetland now is rather leggier than the British type, which is the result of trying to breed for a 'riding type'. Black is not as predominant among show Shetlands as in Britain, and there are very many greys.

Showing is extremely well supported, with up to thirty in-hand classes at each of the six Royal Agricultural Shows (Sydney, Melbourne, Perth, Adelaide, Brisbane and Canberra). There are separate classes for ponies of different heights: up to 8.2 hands (34in), up to 9.2 hands (38in) and up to 10.2 hands (42in). These shows have saddle and harness classes as well. The market for Shetland ponies is very buoyant, as they are widely popular as children's ponies, being of a riding type.

AMERICA

The Americans became very interested in Shetland ponies in the late nineteenth century (*see* Chapter 3). Their enthusiasm was quite astonishing. Dr Elliott of Boston, Massachusetts, an authority on ponies, is quoted as saying:

> The Shetland is the most beautiful, the most reliable in disposition, the freest from defect, and the pony that suffers the least from neglect of any known breeds. He is absolutely without the taint of a vicious trait.[3]

An unnamed American writer of the late nineteenth century stated that 'Children and Shetland ponies seem to have for each other a natural affinity.'[4] Another anonymous quotation from America at about the same time is worth quoting in full, with its amusing emphasis on value for money:

> A boy or girl can get more fun, physical development and ruddy health to the square inch out of a Shetland pony than in any other way, and more real unalloyed happiness than he or she is apt to get out of a fortune in later life.

'If you have a million dollars to spend in giving your child health and happiness, you could not invest it in any way that would accomplish the object better than the investment in a Shetland pony.' The full force of this was impressed upon me by a remark of one of our wealthy merchants, known the world over, and who, had he been so disposed, could have spent a million, by saying that an investment of one hundred and fifty dollars for a Shetland pony had given his child more pleasure and happiness, combined with health, than any he could have made for any amount of money.[5]

So the Americans came and bought as many Shetlands as they could. Mostly they did not come in person but obtained their ponies from consignments sent by dealers in the Islands to dealers on the east coast of America, but a few did make the trip to the Shetlands themselves.

The first shipment of which there is a record is a batch, a stallion and some mares, bought from the Londonderry Stud by Mr Robert Lilburn of Janesville, Wisconsin in 1884.[6] His herd eventually numbered over 500 ponies. Mr Eli Elliot, himself presumably a dealer, bought seventy-five ponies in the Islands in 1885, and two years later, he bought 129 with another man.[7] In 1888 a group of twenty Shetland breeders met in Chicago and formed the American Shetland Pony Club (it is a matter of pride for this society that it is two years older than the 'parent' society in Scotland!). Twenty of the ponies registered in Volume 1 of the British Stud Book in 1890 were exported to America.

The aims of the breeders in America were not the same as in Britain. As described in Chapter 4, the need to keep the size down for the coalmining trade meant that Shetlands were always bred pure and were strictly limited to 42in (most ponies being well under that height). In America, the ponies were bred purely for riding or driving, so there was not the same need to restrict their size; the height limit was eventually set at 46in (11.2 hands). Before long Shetlands were being crossed with other breeds to bring in more height and perhaps freer action. Welsh ponies were used for a riding type, Hackneys for driving. Harness became the most important work for Shetlands, and they were very popular as show harness ponies both in single harness and in teams of four or even six. The Hackney type became more and more predominant in the American Shetlands, and by the 1950s even Shetland enthusiasts had to admit that the ponies were overspecialised:

Many of the breeders of Shetlands have been primarily interested in upgrading style and animation in order to have a high-class harness pony for the show ring. To achieve these ends they have used crosses of the small hackney which has given the desired results but has done nothing to make the animal more suitable for a child's pleasure.[8]

These ponies would not be recognisable as Shetlands to a person who was used to the original Island ponies. They look like Hackneys, and do not suggest any native-pony blood at all.

Many American breeders were worried about this, and eventually the American Shetland Pony Club decided to divide its stud book into two divisions. From 1982 there have been Division A for 'Classic American Shetlands' and Division B for 'Modern Shetlands'. Division A ponies must have both parents registered Shetlands, whereas Division B need only have 50 per cent Shetland blood. However, the 'Classic American Shetland' is still a long way removed from the original Shetland type as bred in Britain. The American height limit is still 46in, and half a century of breeding for light build and high action has had its intended effect.

At the same time a quite different trend has taken place in America. Since the early 1960s a type of animal known as the 'Miniature Horse' has been extremely popular there. In 1962 President Kennedy bought three of them, and they made a very pretty picture standing under the Christmas tree at the White House. These little animals are very much more like Island Shetland ponies, but there have been various different accounts of their origin. According to one, these miniature horses were discovered at the bottom of the Grand Canyon in Arizona in about 1939; they were supposed to be descendants of horses brought over by the Spaniards in the sixteenth century which had become trapped in the Canyon. It was said that 'Lack of subsistence had reduced them to pygmies.'[9] Another story was that miniature horses were bred in the royal courts of Renaissance Europe: 'The trusted royal stable keeper who was instrumental in breeding these Miniatures was very influential and highly respected for his skill and knowledge – he was practically a member of the royal court.'[10]

The truth is that miniature horses (or ponies) were largely the creation of one man, Senor Falabella of Argentina. He set out in the 1950s to breed ponies as small as he could and at first was not prepared to reveal what ponies he had used as foundation stock. It eventually emerged that he had started with Shetlands, but unfor-

135

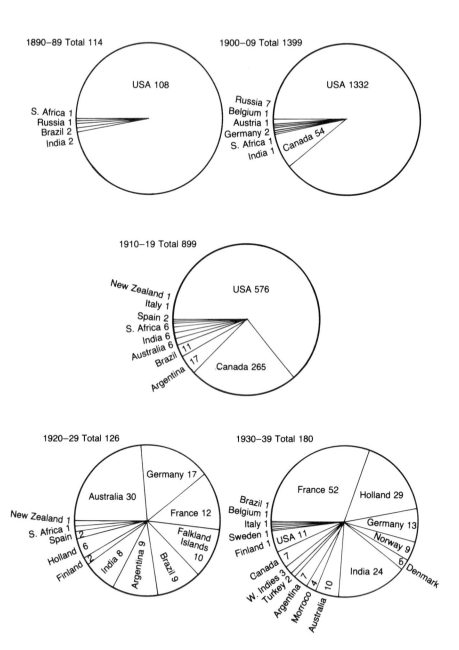

Fig 88   Exports of Shetland ponies to different countries over the past century. (Data from Patterson, 1988.)

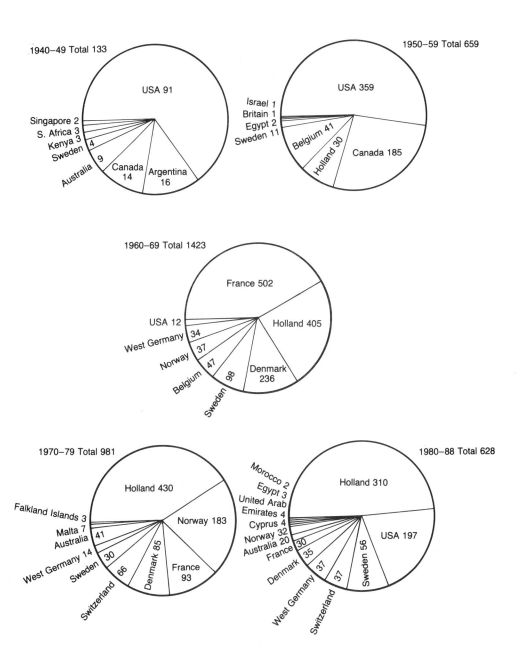

1940–49 Total 133

USA 91

Singapore 2
S. Africa 3
Kenya 3
Sweden
Australia
Canada 14
Argentina 16

1950–59 Total 659

USA 359

Israel 1
Britain 1
Egypt 2
Sweden 11
Belgium 41
Holland 30
Canada 185

1960–69 Total 1423

France 502

USA 12
West Germany 34
Norway 37
Belgium 47
Sweden 98
Holland 405
Denmark 236

1970–79 Total 981

Holland 430

Falkland Islands 3
Malta 7
Australia
West Germany 14
Sweden 30
Switzerland 66
Denmark 85
Norway 183
France 93

1980–88 Total 628

Holland 310

Morocco 2
Egypt 3
United Arab Emirates 4
Cyprus 4
Norway 32
Australia 20
France 30
Denmark 35
West Germany 37
Switzerland 37
Sweden 56
USA 197

137

tunately he had not kept records of the pedigrees of any of his ponies, either the foundation stock or those of his own breeding.[11]

Some of Senor Falabella's ponies have been imported into Britain, where they are known as Falabella horses (a collection of them can be seen at Kilverston Wildlife Park, near Thetford, Norfolk). They are not typical of British Shetland ponies (*see* Chapter 12 for a discussion of the breeding of miniatures). Many more have gone to America, where they are popular as 'Miniature Horses'. These were formerly another division of the American Shetland Pony Club, but are now organised by the separate American Miniature Horse Association. The regulation height for them is 34in, the same as for 'miniatures' in Britain. The Shetland ponies being bought by Americans from British breeders now are entirely in this category.

Many are bought as pets, but there is also a thriving and highly competitive showing scene. Some British-bred ponies have been successful in the American show ring, for instance the filly Birling Silver Slipper (bred by Lionel Hamilton-Renwick) who was second in a class of forty on her first outing, and Toyhorse Windwalker (bred by Mrs Adorian), winner at the 1988 National Show of the American Miniature Horse Association. American enthusiasts also buy Shetland ponies from the studs in Holland.

CANADA

The Canadians were substantial supporters of Shetland ponies at about the time of the First World War. The Douglases wrote:

> In Canada, at the moment, he [the Shetland pony] is in great demand: there he is the school pony; for in the new wheat lands farms are far from the schools, and a pony is the child's conveyance. For this purpose a mount is needed which is easily kept, docile, and hardy, and which can be hitched to a fence during school hours without being critical of the state of the thermometer. The Shetland pony supplies the demand, as if he had been created for that purpose; and Canadian buyers come to Britain year by year to take ponies in increasing numbers.[12]

Canadians were keen buyers of Shetlands again in the 1950s; presumably the ponies were to be pets or riding ponies by that time.

THE NETHERLANDS

Shetland ponies have always been much appreciated by the Dutch, as is witnessed by the fact that Dutch fishermen so often wanted to take them back from their voyages to the Islands. In Holland, Shetland ponies have traditionally been used on the land; they were ideal for taking produce from a market garden to the nearest town. They have now been replaced by motor transport for that work, but they are even more popular than ever as pets and as show ponies. The Dutch breed society, the Nederlandsch Shetland Pony Stamboek, was founded in 1937. Many of the ponies in the Netherlands at that time must have been descendants of the fishermen's ponies as according to the British Stud Book only thirty-five ponies had gone there by 1939.[13] Over the past twenty years, the Netherlands has been the destination of the majority of Shetland ponies being exported. There are more registered Shetlands in the Netherlands than there are in Britain; over there, there are an estimated 8,000 mares. Miniature ponies are popular, now accounting for about 20 per cent of the total.

Fig 89   Dutch-bred stallion Silvester van Stal de Hoeve
(owned by Mr Doevendans), championship winner in 1989.

Traditionally, the Dutch favoured a draft type of Shetland, suitable for their work in harness, but more recently the trend has been towards a lighter type of pony. There are four height classes: mini, up to 86cm (just under 34in); small, 87–92cm (34–6in); middling, 93–98cm (36½–8½in); and large, 99–107cm (39–42in). Each of these has separate show classes. Every year there is an official initial letter for ponies' names: 1988 was C, 1989 was D, etc., and all Dutch-bred ponies have to have names beginning with this letter.

Stallion inspection is even more rigorous in the Netherlands than in Britain. The Stamboek holds an annual stallion show each January at which colts and stallions are inspected by a vet as well as by judges. There are qualifying shows during the previous autumn, at which about two-thirds of the candidates fail. About twenty-five colts get licensed each year, with the numbers evenly distributed among the sizes and colours, and in most cases the licence is only for one year. A full licence runs for three years and is only awarded to 5 per cent of stallions. A licence is never renewable if a stallion is known to have thrown a deformed foal. Premiums of three grades I, II and III are awarded to the successful stallions at the January show, and a supreme champion is chosen.

DENMARK

The Danish stud book began in 1960, and is very well supported by some 250 breeders. The favoured type is a strong-limbed stocky pony, with chestnuts the most numerous followed by blacks. Both mares and stallions must be inspected at the annual selection show in order to be registered. Mares are seen at three years old and again at four; stallions can get a temporary one-year licence when they are two or three years old, but for a full licence they must be four years old and pass a test either ridden or driven. Both mares and stallions receive a rating according to their quality.

SHETLANDS IN THE SUN

Shetland ponies have proved amazingly adaptable in making themselves comfortable in different climates. Southern England is different enough from the Islands, and Shetlands do very well there. They have also been sent to tropical countries for many years. The

Fig 90   Danish-bred colt Skovlundens Ivanhoe,
championship winner in 1988 as a two-year-old (bred by
J. Lassen, owned by C. Christiansen).

first records of this go back to the 1890s, when ponies were sent to
India, South Africa and Brazil. South America became a more
important destination in the years of the First World War, when
seventeen went to Argentina and eleven to Brazil. At about the
same time, Shetlands began to go to southern Europe – two to
Spain, one to Italy. Between the wars the first Shetlands arrived in
the West Indies, and also in North Africa. The Middle East saw its
first Shetlands in the 1950s.

Small numbers of ponies are still exported to tropical or hot
countries and they do very well, but they make the mistake of
growing a winter coat each year which has to be clipped off.

THE FIRST INTERNATIONAL SHOW OF
SHETLAND PONIES

Paris was the venue in December 1988 for the first ever international
show of Shetlands, held under the auspices of the French breed

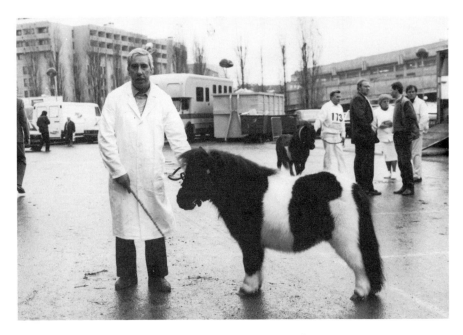

Fig 91 Graham Hughes with his home-bred three-year-old,
Romany Paco, first prize winner in the European
Championships at the first International Show of Shetland
Ponies, Paris, 1988.

society, the Groupement des Eleveurs des Poneys Shetland. Ponies
from ten nations took part. The British contingent consisted of Mrs
Sheila Hinde, who took a third prize in the European Championships with her miniature filly Hippominimus Cassandra, and Mr
Graham Hughes, whose Romany Paco was first in the miniature
three-year-old European Championships, and who also gained a
second place in the World Championships with Paco's sire, Ebony
Prince.

12

Miniature Shetlands

A miniature Shetland pony is one that is 34in or less at maturity. That is all. Unfortunately, however, the subject of miniature Shetlands has given rise to a great deal of debate and some down-right bad feeling. It has to be said at the outset that ponies of this size have occurred in the breed throughout its history. Some of the early reports may be travellers' tales, exaggerating the smallness of the pony for effect, but I am inclined to believe in Miss Edmonston's

Fig 92   Fandango of Wetherden, owned by Lionel Hamilton-Renwick. This 31in stallion was extremely successful in the show ring often winning against standard-sized ponies.

Fig 93   Not just a children's pet: Edwina (owned by Mrs
Adorian) was also a show mare, one of the early winners of the
Gleam Quaich.

30in pony,[1] and there are several ponies, both mares and stallions,
under 34in registered in the first volume of the Stud Book. These
include Tom Thumb 44, the ex-pit pony.

It is also true that since the founding of the Stud Book there have
been breeders who have preferred smaller ponies. Foremost of
these were the Ladies Estella and Dorothea Hope (though they bred
larger ponies too), whose South Park stud was carried on by their
great-niece Lady Joan Gore-Langton. As a third-generation Shetland breeder, Lady Joan had unparalleled knowledge and skill in
breeding miniature ponies, and was the finest spokeswoman in
their cause. Her sudden death in April 1989 was a great loss to the
breed.

SHOW CLASSES FOR MINIATURES

The idea that a miniature is somehow a separate type of pony dates back to the introduction of separate show classes for small ponies. In the 1960s when in-hand showing was booming (*see* Chapter 6) classes of thirty or more were usual, and exhibitors of small ponies felt, with some justification, that they did not get a fair share of the prizes. The first all-Shetland show at Newbury Racecourse (*see* Chapter 6) introduced such a class; stallions were excluded, but the first time they also could be shown was at Newbury in 1968. The class was for 'miniatures, either sex, 2 years old or over, not to exceed 34in at maturity', and there was a trophy, the Gleam Quaich, presented by the Ebony Stud. Separate classes built up slowly; by 1975 there were still only half a dozen, but in 1980 there were more like twenty, with several shows having a youngstock and an adult class for miniatures. Now there are perhaps thirty, but it is noticeable that the large shows – the various Royals and the regionals such as the South of England – do not have miniature classes, nor on the whole do the counties or major shows (Durham County, Montgomeryshire County, and Newbury are the exceptions).

ARE MINIATURES TAKING OVER THE BREED?

Now that there is a height limit for show classes, breeders have a definite size to aim for. This was not the case up until the introduction of these show classes. Previously breeders of small ponies just bred small ponies, and many of their stock matured at 35in or 36in as well as 33in or 34in, and that was perfectly alright. This polarisation of the breed into two different groups, 'miniatures' and 'standards', is reflected in the heights of the ponies registered in the Stud Book over this period. I have compared the heights of ponies registered in 1964, the first year of separate classes, with those in the latest available Stud Book, Volume 88 (1987), twenty-three years later. Fig 96 shows the heights of Section A mares in 1964 and 1987: a mere 12 out of 186, or 6.5 per cent, of mares were miniatures in 1964, and now it is as many as 121 out of 292, or 41 per cent.

Fig 97 gives the comparable figures for stallions and colts registered in 1964 and 1987.[2] In 1964, eight out of fifty-three, that is 15 per cent, were classed as miniatures; by 1987 this had changed to

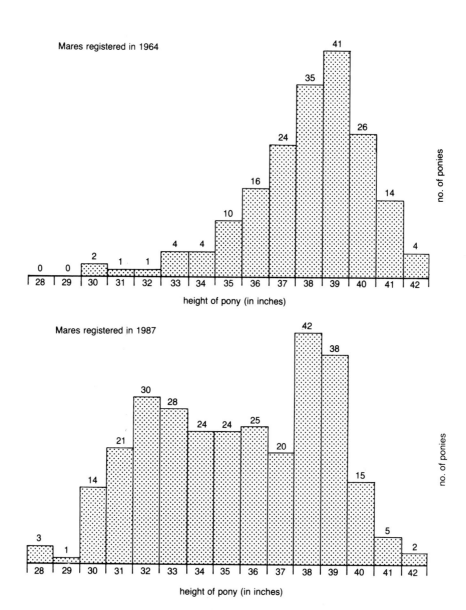

Fig 94   Heights of mares registered in the Stud Book in 1964 and 1987. Miniatures have become much more common, and the breed shows signs of dividing into two quite separate types.

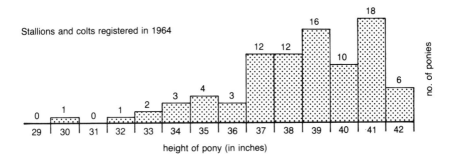

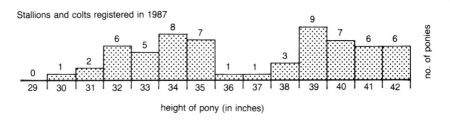

Fig 95 Heights of stallions and colts registered in the Stud
Book in 1964 and 1987.

twenty-two out of sixty-two, or 35 per cent. If stallions and colts of
35in are included (for these are clearly ponies that were meant to be
under 34in but have just overshot the mark), the percentage nowadays is 47 per cent small to 53 per cent standard. It is more
noticeable with the male ponies than the females that the breed has
polarised into two separate sizes: the figure shows that the two most
'fashionable' sizes are 34in and 39in. Stallions of 36in or 37in which
used to be quite numerous have now virtually disappeared, with
only one of each registered in 1987.

To look at it another way, the Under-34in show class was started
in a year when twelve mares and eight male ponies of that size were
registered, i.e. twenty ponies in all. Doubtless not all of them were
of show quality. It was for the benefit of a mere handful of ponies
(belonging to how many owners?) that the miniature classes were
started. One can only speculate as to what would have happened if
the line had been drawn at 36in, not 34in, which would have made
three times as many ponies eligible and put far less pressure on the
breed.

147

MARKET FORCES

It was, of course, not just the lure of success in the show ring that prompted breeders to go for the miniature ponies. It turned out that they were more popular with the customers. To some extent, customers wanted the ponies for the show ring, and felt that it was easier to choose a pony by criteria that they could understand, that is by its very small size or its attractive colouring, than to embark on the esoteric business of knowing which standard black pony was better than which other one. Or, at a more simple level, the customers simply preferred the colours and the smaller size, no matter what might go on in the show ring. It is a fact that the great majority of miniature ponies are coloured. In the 1987 Stud Book, 83 per cent of miniature mares are coloured, and 86 per cent of miniature (including 35in – *see* above) stallions. The comparable figures for standard ponies being mares 46 per cent coloured and stallions 18 per cent.

'Customers' includes not just the British families buying a pony

Fig 96   One of the many ponies that finish a little taller than intended: Firth Gold-n-Ivory (owned and bred by Mrs Berry), registered at 34⅞in.

Fig 97 Toyhorse Treacle, bred by Mrs Adorian: probably the
most expensive Shetland pony in the world.

for the kids to play with but also foreign buyers with money to
spend. The Dutch taste has always been for small ponies, and they
are still important buyers. The most recent Stud Book (1987) shows
that the great majority of ponies exported to Holland are miniatures.
More important still are the Americans, who created a sensation at
the 1987 Reading Sale by raising the prices of miniature filly foals to
unprecedented heights. No fewer than ten fillies fetched more than
£1,000, with a top price of 5,000 guineas (£5,250) for Mr Hughes's
piebald Romany Prospect. All these ponies went to America. Even
these prices are not as high as some in private transactions, and the
best-ever price for a Shetland pony is believed to be Mrs Adorian's
sale of Toyhorse Treacle, a yearling colt expected to mature at 31in,
who was sold to an American breeder for US $20,000 in 1988.

It is the fact that there is so much money in miniatures that has
caused the increase in their numbers. But does it matter? It does,
and to understand why, one has to look at the underlying biology.

THE GENETIC BACKGROUND

To begin with, it is obvious that there are many miniature Shetlands that are of excellent conformation and of absolutely true Shetland type. It is also true that many of these ponies are ridden and driven and that they are just as capable of doing useful work as the larger ponies. But there are also a considerable number of miniatures that are not of good conformation and not of the Shetland type.

The characteristic Shetland was evolved for the particular environment in the Islands. The typical Shetland is that size because of its genetic make-up, and if you want a larger size, you must cross with a genetically bigger pony. If you want a smaller size, you must breed from ponies that are *genetically* small. A characteristic such as height can be influenced by the environment, but a pony that has been environmentally caused to be small will not pass its smallness down to its offspring. The runt of a litter of piglets or puppies has the same genetic make-up as its larger brothers and sisters but has been stunted by being in a disadvantageous position in the uterus. You could, and would, breed normal-sized offspring from such an animal. Restriction on an animal's growth may take place after it is born (this is much more usual). A foal that is weaned too early or not adequately fed will certainly be smaller than others as a yearling and may never catch up as an adult, but, again the animal is genetically normal and if it is bred from it will have normal-sized offspring. (A typical case of this was recounted to me by a breeder of standard-sized ponies. She came across a filly that she had sold as a foal and was horrified by its small size and narrow frame. She bought it back and did what she could to feed it up, but at three years old it was not able to catch up much growth, if any. Put in-foal as a four-year-old, it produced the first of many normal foals that inherited the size their mother would have had if properly reared.) A bout of illness will have the same effect on growth as undernourishment. In these cases, the smallness is acquired from external conditions, and is therefore known as an 'acquired characteristic'. It is an important principle of genetics that acquired characteristics cannot ever be inherited. This was first proved by a German contemporary of Darwin's, August Weismann, and has been continually confirmed in scientific experiments.[3] Thus a pony genetically normal-sized but made small through environmental factors will be useless for breeding small ponies: it will breed to the size of its genes, not the size that its own body happens to be.

DEFECTIVE PONIES

A different situation is presented by a pony whose genes for height are normal but who has a gene (or genes) causing some other defect. This might very well be a defect of the metabolism, preventing the pony from extracting nourishment from its food properly. Such a pony would not thrive no matter how well it was looked after, and it would end up a small pony. It would also almost certainly end up a bad-looking pony, as it would not have reached the symmetry of growth of a properly matured pony. Ponies of this sort should not be used for breeding small stock, because they are small on account of their defect. But the important thing to note is that they *would* pass on their smallness to their offspring, as the cause of their smallness is in their genes not their environment.

NEOTENY

The science of genetics has not yet progressed to the point where the individual genes for each characteristic of a complicated animal like a human or a pony can be identified (though they can for viruses and bacteria and unicellular animals). However, the principles are quite well understood in outline, and all the experimental data from laboratory animals hold good when applied to larger animals, including ponies. One finding is that there is a gene (or more likely a group of genes) that causes the animal to retain some of its juvenile features in adult life, even though it is fully mature: this is called *neoteny* (pronounced neott'eny, to rhyme with 'botany'). This may very well provide the explanation for the size of some small ponies. Growing slowly, they do not get to normal size before maturity sets in, and they retain several features of a juvenile pony, for example the rounded forehead, narrow chest and steep pasterns. This certainly seems to fit with the fact that some miniature ponies grow very slowly, and with the juvenile characteristics that some of them show. Breeding from these ponies to get more small ponies will work, as the smallness is caused genetically (by the neoteny gene(s)), not environmentally. Neoteny is not necessarily an unsoundness in itself, because the pony is simply carrying into adult life the characteristics of a normal, sound juvenile pony. But the adult neoteny pony does look notably different from a pony of standard type. It was the neoteny type of pony that was used by

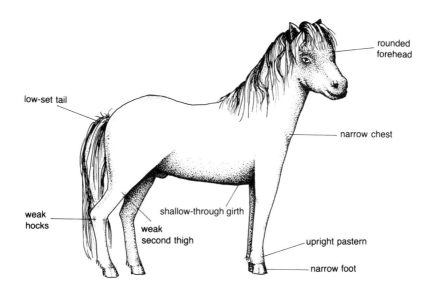

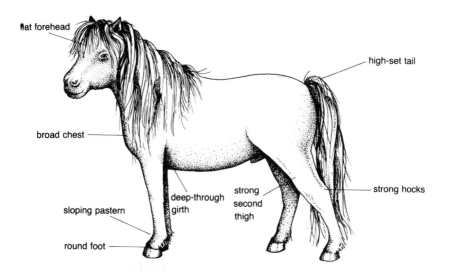

Fig 98   Diagram to show the difference between a neotenous
pony and a true-type miniature.

Senor Falabella to found his line of miniature horses (*see* Chapter 11).

A most interesting light is thrown on to the neoteny type of pony by some research done by the great Austrian zoologist Konrad Lorenz, founder of the science of animal behaviour. He discovered that whatever type of animal one is considering, humans are more likely to feel affection for the ones that have juvenile features.[4] Therefore, it is only to be expected that neotenous miniature ponies are the most popular with people who are looking for a pony to be a pet.

TRUE-TYPE SMALL PONIES

Finally, there are some Shetlands who mature at 34in or less who are that size simply because they have inherited all the genes for small size. There are probably at least six different genes for size, and for a pony to get all of the small ones together is an outside chance if you are breeding at random, but quite a good chance if you are breeding from ponies you already know to have genes for small size. These are the ideal for breeding miniatures, as they have no unsoundness and they do not have the neoteny characteristics to make them look unlike breed type.

The table sets out these four basic types of small ponies. It can be seen that although the end product is the same in all cases, i.e. an under-34in pony, the underlying causes are different. Type 1 is, as already noted, not genetically caused and will therefore not breed small offspring. Type 2 is genetically caused but should not be used for breeding as the pony is in fact defective. Types 3 and 4 are both suitable for breeding small stock, but they are of quite different

The Genetic Background to the Different Types of Miniature Ponies

Type	Size Genes	Cause of Pony's Smallness	Heritable?
1.	normal	undernourishment or illness	no
2.	normal	defective metabolic gene	yes
3.	normal	neoteny gene(s)	yes
4.	small	small size genes	yes

genetic make-up, and crossing them together may give unsatisfactory results.

DWARFING

One gene that is *not* involved in miniature Shetlands, apparently, is the dwarfing gene. The typical effect of this is to shorten the limb bones, especially the cannons, while leaving the rest of the skeleton almost normal. If this gene were the cause of the reduced size of miniature ponies, they would be proportionately shorter in the leg than the standard type. They are, however, almost never short-legged but often longer-legged proportionately than standards, and the reason for this is the neoteny effect referred to above. To be relatively long-legged is a juvenile feature, and ponies with the neoteny gene(s) will tend to retain it.[5]

UNSOUND OR NOT?

The difficulty comes in deciding whether or not a pony with the neoteny characteristics should be regarded as unsound. All the features that distinguish these ponies are in fact the normal features of juvenile ponies but carried through into adult life. If the features are normal and do not constitute unsoundness in a juvenile pony, can they be said to amount to unsoundness in an adult? The answer must be yes, because these ponies never get the maturity of limbs that would enable them to work. The reason that one does not ride or drive a two or three-year-old pony is that its skeleton is not mature; without sufficient bone and without the correct angles of the joints, especially the hocks, the pony does not have enough strength to perform work. The neotenous type of miniature pony remains in this state throughout its life. (The miniature pony that is correctly formed (Type 4 in the table), is of course as sound and capable of work as any other Shetland.)

If a decision was made to try to eradicate the neotenous ponies from the breed, the obvious first step would be to refuse licences to any colts that showed this trait. But here is the difficulty: these neotenous ponies have nothing to show that is not normal *for a young pony*. It could be extremely difficult, if not impossible, to distinguish a normal two-year-old colt from one that was in fact

Fig 99   Mr and Mrs Hughes' Ebony Prince, second prize
winner in the World Championships in Paris, 1988. (Photo by
courtesy of *Congleton Chronicle*.)

neotenous. All colts still have a lot of growing to do between two
and maturity, and they all look narrower in the chest and shakier in
the joints at two than they will as adults. It would be hard to be sure
at two years old, but easier at three. A case could be made for
automatically deferring for a year the inspection of any colt who was
32in or under at two years old.

The fact is that very considerable numbers of registered Shetland
ponies are of a type that is nowhere near the ideal described by Mr
Meiklejohn one hundred years ago. His words are quoted at the
very beginning of this book, and it is worth bearing them in mind
when thinking about miniatures. This problem needs to be tackled
with goodwill and farsightedness by Shetland breeders and the

Council that they elect. It is in everyone's long-term interest to preserve the true Shetland type, as was so clearly seen by the Douglases over eighty years ago: 'Anything which tends to make the pony merely an oddity and a toy, and to take it out of the category of useful or usable horses, is fatal to the prospects of the breed and should be resisted by breeders and judges.'[6]

13

Buying and Keeping a Shetland Pony

WHERE TO BUY

If you have never had a Shetland pony before, you will perhaps not know where to start looking for one. But you do know what you want it for: a first pony for your child, a driving pony for yourself, possibly several ponies as the foundation of a stud. You will also probably have decided whether you like miniature ponies or standard-sized ones. Whatever it is that you are looking for, do get expert advice. Do not be tempted to cut corners by rushing off and buying the first 'adorable Shetland filly' that you see advertised in the local paper (some good ponies do come on to the market in this way, but a great many more poor ones – beware).

The best way to start is to contact the Shetland Pony Stud-Book Society and get a copy of their magazine.[1] Look through the stud advertisements, most of which are illustrated, and pick out the ones that have the sort of ponies you like and are within reach. Go and see more than one breeder, ideally. Obviously each breeder will want to sell you one of their ponies, but they will also be generous with advice about Shetlands in general, and you are sure to learn a great deal about the breed.

If you want to buy a pony ready schooled for riding or driving, it is as well to ask that the pony should be out at grass when you arrive. Say that you want to see him caught, brought into the yard, groomed (including having his feet done), saddled or harnessed and put-to. It is obviously essential that the pony is absolutely quiet for all these procedures, particularly if it is to be a child's pony. It is as well, too, to ask to see him loaded into a box or trailer – it would be very annoying to buy the creature and then find that you could not take him home (this has happened!).

Then you will want to see him put through his paces as a riding or

157

driving pony. This must include going out on to the road and meeting traffic. Shetlands are not timid and are not usually frightened of even the largest juggernauts, but you must satisfy yourself that this pony is all right; if in any doubt at all turn him down.

Buying a riding or driving pony privately and trying it out as above is probably the best way to do it. You may even be allowed to have the pony on a week or fortnight's trial, which is better still. If you buy at an auction you will have only a limited opportunity to try the pony out, and of course the animal may well not give a true account of itself because of being upset by the unfamiliar surroundings. However, if you are confident enough of your eye for a pony (or have a friend whose opinion you trust) you are to a large extent protected by the auctioneer's warranty. Any pony described in the catalogue as 'warranted quiet to ride' or 'warranted quiet to drive' must be so. It must be sound, traffic-proof and vice-free, and if it turns out that it is not, you are able to take it back (usually you have forty-eight hours in which to do this). Be very careful: a pony merely described as 'quiet to drive' is *not* warranted, neither do such phrases as 'has been ridden away' or 'has been driven by a child' have any legal significance.

BUYING FOR A STUD

If you are intending to buy some ponies to set up a stud, you will have to learn a little about pedigrees. Ideally you will go to some shows (dates are given in the Shetland Pony Stud-Book Society Magazine) to see which are the ponies you like and to learn which breeding lines they have come from. Then you can go and visit the studs that produce that sort of pony. You are bound to have a wonderful time doing this, as breeders are without exception delighted to show off their ponies and talk about them.

Perhaps you will want to start with a few mares or in-foal fillies; perhaps you will want to buy foals. Choosing a foal is a highly skilled business. To see a future champion in that fluffy stiff-legged bundle takes a really fine eye (and a bit of luck – there are ugly ducklings among ponies as in anything else). You will have to go on its pedigree to a large extent: is its mother the sort of pony you are trying to breed? has its father sired other stock that you can look at? You may be particularly interested in colour, and here again is a difficulty, as some ponies are quite a different colour as foals than

Fig 100   Choosing a foal is difficult: they can have such
overpowering charm! This is Firth Pineapples with her dam
Firth Primrose, both owned and bred by Mrs Berry.

they will be as adults. Roans and many greys acquire their white
hairs gradually, and black ponies are a mousey grey-brown for their
first year.

When it comes to buying a foal, an auction can be a very good
idea. The pedigree, which is after all the most important piece of
information, will be given in the catalogue. Some very fine foals
indeed can be bought in the autumn sales in the Islands, at prices
that are very attractive to the purchasers but make one weep for the
vendors. The average price of a filly foal at the Lerwick sale in 1987
was £46, a colt foal £15. Prices are much higher at the annual sale of
Shetland ponies held in Reading each October, where the 1988
average figures were filly foals £419 and colt foals £82.[2] These prices
are very much influenced by the presence of purchasers from

159

overseas; of the nineteen highest-priced filly foals, eight went abroad. Much better value is to be had at the Reading sale for older colts and stallions. In 1988 really well bred stallions, with prizes or even championships to their credit, could be had for under £200.

Shetlands are generally speaking extremely healthy, and perhaps for that reason many buyers do not insist on a vet's certificate. It is also a question of the value of the pony compared to the cost of a full veterinary inspection, which could be as much as £80. However, if the pony is intended for a very active life as a child's pony or for driving it is just as well to make sure.

KEEPING A SHETLAND PONY

Basically a Shetland pony is an equine like any other, and has the same requirements as any other. However, they do tend to suffer from two opposite misunderstandings which can lead to them being badly kept. The first is that they are so hardy that they can live on practically nothing; the second is that they are almost like household pets and are delighted to be fed on titbits. Neither of these is true.

GRAZING

A Shetland pony needs decent grazing. The ideal is to keep them in conditions resembling their native islands, that is on rough pasture or in large fields where they can move around a lot in search of their daily rations. They can be kept in small enclosures successfully, but care must be taken that the pasture does not become 'horse-sick' from being too intensively grazed. It is not possible to graze the same ground indefinitely with ponies; it must be rested from time to time and ideally some other sort of animal grazed there. It is also very important with small paddocks to be punctilious in picking up the ponies' droppings so as to minimise the risk of infestation with worms.

WORMS

Worms are a great scourge of Shetlands as of other ponies, particularly where they are kept on intensively grazed land. The common

Mrs Handcock's Courtier of Woodbury and Apollo.

The Reading Sale – a child says goodbye to her pony.

Multiple turnout. Mrs Carlisle's unicorn of Eastlands
Sunstroke, Tibthorpe Peneleway and Five Squared of
Crooklands, driven to a wagonette built in about 1883.
(Photograph: Anthony Reynolds)

Tandem driving. Mrs Simpson's Snowville Merlin and
Benjamin Bear taking part in the London Harness Horse
Parade in Regent's Park.

roundworm, which looks rather like a large white earthworm, looks alarming but is not as harmful as the red worm, a small (about ½in) thin wriggling worm, which causes not just digestive problems but general loss of condition. A pony that has an infestation of worms may show no sign of the actual worms in its droppings because only the worms' eggs are being passed in the dung, and they are invisible to the naked eye. The safest thing is to dose the pony regularly with a worm powder.

LAMINITIS

If Shetland ponies are kept on rich pasture there can be a problem with laminitis, particularly in the spring. The only answer is to restrict severely the amount of grazing available to the ponies. Ponies kept on good pasture can also become too fat. Fat ponies are inefficient at their work (if they have any), are extremely uncomfortable for a small child to ride and are likely to develop skin trouble and faulty action which may even result in permanent unsoundness. Once again the ponies must be restricted in their access to

Fig 101   A pony tethered where it has shade and shelter.

161

grazing; it may even be necessary to keep them in a box or yard for most of the day and only allow them an hour or two at grass. Another possibility is tethering, though the pony must be watched to see that he does not get tangled up. A chain is better than a rope for tethering because if it gets wound round a leg the loop falls to the ground and the pony can just step out of it.

MINERALS

It is of course essential that there is a constant supply of good water. Equally essential is a mineral lick. Shetland ponies do not seem to appreciate the benefits of a roofed shelter, and will not go into one even in the wettest and bitterest weather. However, they must have something to use as a wind-break against the prevailing winds. If their field does not already have a wall or thick hedge to provide this, a few yards of hurdles or planked fencing must be put up. In summer, they like to have a shady place to stand in (this may be the only time they will condescend to go inside a roofed shelter), and they will gather under a tree or in the shade of a hedge or rock. Artificial shade (hurdles are again useful) should be provided if needed.

FENCING

A word about fencing. Shetland ponies are intelligent and inquisitive creatures, and if they are bored they may set about trying to escape to amuse themselves (this is a worse problem with a solitary Shetland than it is with a herd). The fencing will need to be very secure to keep them in. Perhaps the ideal is a thick, old-established hedge. A wall is good, too, though Shetlands are adept at scrambling over the dry-stone kind if it has a low spot. The post-and-rails fence that is so good for larger ponies and horses is *not* Shetland-proof as foals can pop under the bottom rail in an instant, and even adult ponies can squeeze through unless you put in another rail. Barbed-wire fencing, unfortunately very common because it is cheap and effective for cattle, is bad for ponies in general; they can and do get scratched or cut, and they also sometimes rub off the whole of their manes; foals can usually get under the bottom wire. Barbed-wire is even worse when it is not well maintained: rusty

Fig 102 The fence kept this mare in but *not* her foal: Black
Beauty of Luckdon, formerly owned by the author.

strands of wire dangling loosely can be extremely dangerous.
Sheep-netting is much better and although it is more expensive it
does not have to be tensioned up so thoroughly. Foals cannot slip
through, and ponies cannot put their heads through to rub their
manes. A pony might put a foot through the mesh, but an unshod
pony would probably have no difficulty in pulling it out again (a
shod one might catch the wire between its shoe and its hoof).
Electric fencing is good too, and you can move it around to change
the run that the ponies have.

Checking that no pony has escaped or caught itself up in the fence
is just one of the things that must be done on the daily inspection.
Look to see that all the ponies are well; you are looking not only for
injuries or lameness but also for signs of a pony being listless or off

163

its food. Check the water – horrendous things can happen with pollution these days.

WINTER FEEDING

In winter, Shetland ponies can manage without feeding *only* if they have access to a very wide area of grazing, and in practice very few ponies are kept in such conditions. How soon to begin feeding in the autumn depends on the amount of grass remaining which will vary from year to year and according to how heavily stocked the grazing is, but usually the middle of October is about the right time. Shetland ponies seem to prefer meadow hay to the rye mixture sort. It is worth taking the trouble to keep the hay off the ground somehow, by using hay-nets or racks; unfortunately, the commercially available hay-racks are too high (the ponies look most uncomfortable reaching up and blinking as the seeds fall in their eyes), so you may have to improvise. Make sure that the ponies can feed well apart, so that they do not kick each other. Shetlands are also fond of

Fig 103   Mares eating hay in the snow. These are owned by Mesdames Stevenson.

root vegetables – swedes, turnips or carrots – which are extremely nourishing and make a welcome change of diet in the winter months. Do not feed any hard food (oats, barley or pony-nuts) to adult ponies. They do not need it unless they are being worked every day. Even a pony that is doing a day or two a week working is far better off doing it on adequate rations of hay or roots rather than corn which will make it overheated and hard to manage.

Shetland ponies should never be washed in winter; washing removes the natural grease from the coat so that it is no longer waterproof. If you have to make a Shetland presentable when it is in full winter coat there is nothing for it but just to brush off the mud with a dandy-brush. A well-brushed-through mane and tail make a surprisingly large impact on the pony's general appearance, so concentrate on these! If the pony gets heated up in the course of his outing, as he may well do with his thick coat, make sure he comes home cool, and rub him down to dry him before you turn him out. Shetlands are very tough but it would be stupid to turn out any pony hot and wet.

If you are working your Shetland pony really hard in the winter, for instance hunting once a week or driving long distances, you may find that he needs a clip. Do the minimum, because Shetlands miss their thick coat very much when it comes off, and you may find that if a pony has to stand around even for a minute or two after he has got hot he will start shivering. Just a few clippers-widths under the girth may be enough to keep a hard-working pony cool without letting him get chilly when he is standing.

NOT HOUSEHOLD PETS

Shetlands are the most attractive and affectionate creatures, and many of them become as attached to their owners as any dog. I have never met anyone who has kept a Shetland who has not admitted to having it in the house at one time or another. However, it is one thing to have a pony make visits to the house, and quite another to expect it to behave like a cat or a dog. Perhaps the most important factor is diet: it is extremely important that the Shetland pony lives on its natural diet and does not get filled up with sugar-lumps, cucumber sandwiches and bits of chocolate. Another aspect of this is transport. Shetland ponies must travel in a proper box or trailer, and not in the back of a car.

Fig 104 A Shetland clipped for hunting. This picture of Master Charles Trigg on Icknield Sherbert out with the West Waterford was taken many years ago.

SHOEING

If a pony is doing work of any sort he will have to be shod. Only the lightest hacking round the fields off the roads can be done by an unshod pony, even though it used to be believed (by no less an authority than Glenda Spooner, for example), that 'here is a breed that can do without shoes if any can'.[3] Ponies without shoes need to have their feet trimmed every ten or twelve weeks. Your blacksmith will probably grumble about having to do this for Shetlands, because their legs are so short that he will have to stand on his head to reach down to them.

INOCULATIONS

Every pony should have an anti-tetanus inoculation, which must be regularly boosted. If the pony is likely to come into contact with others it should also have flu vaccine, which though not 100 per cent effective does give protection against this disease which is very troublesome in some years.

14

Breeding and Breaking
Shetland Ponies

The Douglases said that 'The Shetland pony here is to be treated as a natural – practically a wild – herd of animals.'[1] To a large extent this is true, and any breeder who has enough space to treat a herd in this way is lucky. But in one important way, it is not true, which is that the breeder must segregate some ponies at some times, to prevent unplanned matings, to carry out weaning of foals, etc. So the prerequisite for breeding ponies is enough space. Even if you do not intend to keep your own stallion you will need to be able to separate one group of ponies from another, so you must have an adequate number of separate enclosures, ideally set apart at some distance.

Many people begin by buying in-foal mares, but if you are starting from scratch (i.e. fillies bought as foals) the first decision is how soon your fillies can be put in foal. The 'official' time is when they are three years old (this is official in that a mare with a foal must be four years old for the show ring). However, no less an authority than Major Cox has said that 'If the fillies are well grown and well developed at two there is no reason why they should not be put to the horse to foal down the following year when they are three.'[2] The important thing is that they are really well grown; there is no excuse for impatient or greedy breeders putting two-year-old fillies in foal who are of only average maturity. It is of course unthinkable for a filly to be mated as a yearling, even though some of them are already sexually mature at that age.

STALLIONS

It is almost universal practice to run a stallion with his mares for the summer. Shetland stallions are renowned for their good temper, and there is never any problem with leaving them in charge of mares and foals. Do not put the mares to the stallion too early in the year: gestation is eleven months, and you do not want foals to arrive earlier than April the following year, so do not put them together until May. Equally, you do not want foals born so late in the autumn that they are too small to be weaned; any foal born later than the end of July would be a problem in this way, so the stallion should not be left with the mares after the end of August. It need hardly be said that none of the animals in the breeding herd should be shod. A fair amount of kicking and pawing is part of the normal business, and quite harmless with bare hooves, though potentially dangerous with shoes.

MARES

Breeding females will be either in-foal mares, yeld mares (that is, mature mares who have previously had a foal but are not in foal this year), or maidens. These can all go in together with the stallion, and there is no reason why in-foal mares should not be left with the stallion up to the time of foaling as he is not going to do any harm to mare or foal. There are two caveats. Maiden fillies can be a nuisance, pestering the stallion and behaving aggressively towards the other mares and fillies if they get any share of his attention. This does not happen with every filly, but it is not unusual, and in such cases the filly should be taken away when she has been served and returned after three weeks when she is next in season (ideally, she should be put somewhere out of earshot, as she can go on being quite troublesome by calling to the stallion all the time and distracting him from his duties). Older yeld mares can be jealous of other mares with their foals; an experienced mother will be able to cope with them, but a mare having her first foal may have it stolen from her before she knows what is happening. Again, you will need enough room to keep both parties separate (though not out of earshot in this case).

FOALING

Shetland mares seldom have difficulty in foaling, and it is best to leave them alone to get on with it. However, it is imperative to have

169

the mare somewhere where you can keep a constant watch on her just in case things go wrong. It is perfectly alright for her to stay in with the stallion if his field happens to be close to your house, but otherwise you must bring her up to a paddock close at hand when you think she is near her time. (She may beat you to it.) If all goes well, leave her alone to deal with matters herself; just watch to make sure that the foal is suckling and that it has passed faeces. Occasionally the foal has to be held to the mare to get it to suckle, and it may have a blocked lower bowel which can be unblocked easily. If the mare is in difficulties with her delivery, do not hesitate to call the vet: unskilled intervention can do more harm than good, and you could kill your mare as well as her foal when both or at least one could have been saved.

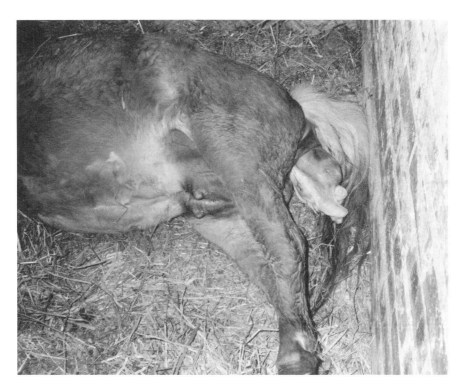

Figs 105–Fig 110   This sequence of photographs of one of Mr and Mrs Hughes' mares shows the birth of a foal from the first sight of its feet and nose to its first attempt to suckle. It is very sad to tell that the mare rejected the foal, and the foal refused to drink from a bottle. It died twenty-four hours later.

Fig 106

Fig 107

Fig 108

Fig 109

Fig 110

In the summer the yearlings look beautiful in their first proper summer coats, and the foals play around as skittishly as lambs. (It would be a pity to have only one foal, as it would have no one to play with.) The mares eat prodigiously, as they must to produce enough milk for the foal; it is hard to remember looking at the neat little dugs that Shetland mares have, that they are making nearly as much milk as a cow.

Foals start to graze when they are only a few weeks old, though grazing is not a significant part of their nourishment at that time. By the time they are six months old and ready to be weaned, they will be eating a good deal of grass.

WEANING

Weaning is a lot easier if the foals are already not just well handled but halter-broken and trained to lead quietly. Catch the mare and lead her and her foal out of the field to some other place (ideally

Fig 111   Well-trained foals at weaning time. These are Mrs
Whitaker's at the Seva stud.

grass, not a yard) where you can have a lesson undisturbed. The
mare has nothing to be worried about, so she will stand tied up
while you get the foal to accept a headcollar being put on. For the
next lesson, try leading the foal around a little, keeping close beside
it and *never* dragging it along. It is easiest if you have another person
to lead the mare around while you lead the foal, as it will naturally
follow its dam and will hardly notice that it is learning how to be
led. Foals as young as three weeks old can learn this perfectly well.

Do not forget that what is charming behaviour in a little foal is
going to be a great deal less charming when the pony is grown up,
e.g. things like rubbing its head up and down your leg or putting a
front foot up to your waist. It is not fair to encourage these sweet
little tricks now when you are going to have to discourage them later
on.

174

At weaning time, when they are about six months old, the foals are separated from their dams and taken to some place where they are out of earshot. This is a very stressful time for both parties, and is made infinitely worse for both if they can still hear each other. You may have to resort to borrowing some grazing from a neighbour to get the mares far enough away. All remarks about Shetland-proof fencing apply twice as strongly at weaning time: mares and foals will be desperate to get to each other. Send the mares off, and keep the foals at home. They are the ones that need careful watching, because you must be sure that they are coping with their new diet. They will already be accomplished at grazing, but now they must eat their hard food to substitute for milk. Arrange things so that there cannot be fights at feeding-time, with the greediest foal grabbing more than its share. Foals are best kept outside day and night; provided they have shelter they will not suffer from cold no matter how hard the weather is, but they must be generally fed with both hay and hard food. They will also need vitamin supplements.

Do not neglect the mares. They will be in discomfort because they are still in milk; they will soon stop producing milk, and soonest if left alone, but in some cases a mare's bag can become so distended that she is suffering severe pain and must be relieved by having some milk drawn off. They are also about half-way through their next pregnancy, and need good feeding to both nourish their unborn foals and to bring themselves through the winter in good shape. An ample supply of hay is usually all the mares need, as the Shetland is an exceptionally thrifty animal, but keep a watch on all the mares and if one seems to need extra food see that she gets it.

YOUNGSTOCK

Youngstock – that is to say yearlings and two to three-year-olds – present further problems of segregation. You can make things easier for yourself by never keeping any foals through the winter so that you never have any youngstock. That is a sensible policy, but before long you will breed a foal so good that you will want to keep it. In the case of a colt, you will have to be honest with yourself when he is a yearling: is he really good enough to pass his inspection as a stallion? If not, have him cut sooner rather than later. As a gelding, he can be put in with your fillies. If you decide to keep him entire until he can have his inspection at two years old, you will have to

175

Fig 112   Stallions and colts running together without trouble.
These are Mrs Staveley's. (Photo by courtesy of *Yorkshire Post*.)

keep him away from the fillies even as a yearling. He will be happier
with some company, which might be another entire colt, a stallion
not being used at stud, or a gelding. Shetland entires are good-
tempered and very seldom get into serious fights with one another,
and even senior stallions will join in the friendly sparring that colts
go in for all the time. It seems to do them nothing but good.

The youngstock fillies can spend the winter with the mares, but in
the summer when the latter go to the stallion, the fillies will remain
on their own. Do not put them so near either to the stallion or to the
young colts (if you have any) that they can amuse themselves by
sexual teasing. Youngstock of either sex needs hard food through
the second and third winter to bring their growth and maturation
on. They, as foals, do not need to be brought in at night.

In the old days of enormous studs kept on wide ranges of land,
the breeding ponies were as good as wild. There is no reason for this
to be the case nowadays, and every reason for it not to be. For one
thing, you want to be able to catch each pony regularly to do its feet;

you may also want to catch a pony in an emergency of one sort or another (perhaps it has broken out of its field, or it has what looks like a cut). The early lessons that the foal had before weaning can usefully be continued with yearlings. Even if you never intend to use the pony for riding or driving it should learn the following: to be led, to stand tied up, to have its feet picked up and trimmed, and to be touched all over (ideally groomed as well).

BREAKING AND SCHOOLING

But let us hope that most Shetland ponies *will* go on to do some work. They must be properly broken in and schooled. The reputation that they have had at some times in the past for being bad-tempered and tricky has been entirely the result of their owners' idleness in assuming that such clever ponies do not need any training. This was recognised as long ago as 1856 by that great admirer of Shetland ponies, Miss Eliza Edmonston:

> These humours are the results of the absence of all breaking in or training . . . From our ample experience of the dispositions and habits of the Shetland pony, indeed, in this, his unsophisticated state, we are persuaded, that any mischievous or vicious propensities, of which we have sometimes heard him accused, have been superinduced by artificial culture and improper management.[3]

And yet even people as experienced with Shetland ponies as Dr and Mrs Douglas felt that training could be got through with a very small amount of time and effort:

> Breaking is usually no difficult matter. A couple of lessons in leading, three in reins, and three in the shafts, with probably one severe conflict of wills in the whole process, will generally break a Shetland pony.[4]

True, they admit that the pony would need its mouth and manners made before it would be a suitable ride for a child, but this attitude that a Shetland can learn anything in no time is still too prevalent. It is not fair on the ponies: they deserve a proper training.

It is not in the least necessary to have 'one severe conflict of wills': a Shetland pony is affectionate and trusting, and is keen to please its

177

owner. If the pony fails to do what you want, that is because it has not understood, and that is your fault for not making yourself clear. (That, of course, is the real reason why training animals makes some people lose their temper; they realise, deep down, that the problem is their own stupidity, not the animal's, and what could be more exasperating than that?) Never get angry, and do not punish the pony for doing things wrong. Fear of punishment is one way to train an animal but it is a bad one because it destroys the creature's trusting nature, which can never be restored. The pony's wish to please you is all you need.

It is natural, though not actually necessary for the purpose of training, to want to give the pony a reward if it has been good or has learnt quickly. It is well worth making it an invariable rule that the titbit is only given from a bucket or scoop or bowl; if the pony sees you fishing in your pocket for the sugar-lump or piece of carrot, he will rightly conclude that your pocket is full of the things, and will begin to ask for them by nibbling at your coat. This can be quite annoying, to say the least, but to a child or a non-horsey adult it can be really frightening behaviour.

Lessons for the Shetland pony who is to be ridden will proceed as for any other riding pony, that is to say that once it has been trained to be led in a headcollar it will learn to wear first its bridle then its saddle. For the bridle, there is something to be said for using a rubber snaffle bit, which is not such an affront to the mouth as a metal bit and will give plenty of control if the pony's mouth is never spoiled by bad handling. As for the saddle, Shetlands are lucky in that they can wear a felt-pad saddle, which has no problems of fitting and does not feel so constraining as a saddle with a tree. Do up the girth loosely the first time and tighten it up later.

A riding pony must be traffic-proof, and its lessons in facing traffic should be part of its training at an early stage. The ideal way to get the first stage over is to graze the pony in a field beside a main road, but even this is not quite the same for the pony as meeting the lorries, etc. face-to-face in the road or having them come up from behind when he is not allowed to turn round and look. Take the pony out for walks along the road in his saddle and bridle until he is absolutely quiet.

Meanwhile his education continues with learning to respond to control via the bit, by being driven in long reins (a Shetland pony is a nice animal for this from the trainer's point of view, as you can see right over his head, unlike a full-sized horse that only gives you a

Fig 113 Breaking in a pony for riding: getting him to accept
the bridle. Mrs Toomer-Harlow demonstrates with Hose
Viyella.

view of its tail). Next comes the stage at which you place some
weight on the saddle. You need something weighing perhaps 15 or
20lb and something that will stay firmly in place. A racing weight-
cloth is ideal, but an old-fashioned sack half-full of stones or potatoes and held on with a strap going right round over the girth would
do. Lead the pony in tight circles with the load on him so that he can
feel what it is like to have weight on his back when his spine is
flexing. Most ponies do not mind this at all.

You have now come to the only difficult moment in breaking a
Shetland pony for riding. The difficulty is that now you want a real
rider to 'back' him, and that rider must be confident and accomplished. If you are very lucky you will know of a twelve or thirteen-
year-old who will spare you some time, but most of these riders are

Fig 114   Hose Panto going well in long reins.

Fig 115   A light adult is an ideal rider for a Shetland (Hose Panto).

too busy with their Grade JA jumpers or whatever to bother with your little Shetland. It is therefore better to get a small adult to do it for you (you may be small enough yourself). Do not worry about the pony not being up to your weight: a fully-grown Shetland pony (and you will not want to be doing this training with a pony less than four years old) is up to a considerable amount of weight since what determines weight-carrying ability is the amount of bone the animal has, and a Shetland can match many a hunter in that respect. The problem for an adult riding a Shetland is that their legs are in the wrong place for giving the aids. Never mind, shorten the stirrups as much as you can bear, and ride the pony yourself. The important thing is for him to learn the other half of the aids – the ones that come from seat and leg – and to get used to obeying a person seated on top of him when up till now all the humans in his world have stood upon the ground.

You can then develop its balance and obedience, doing such exercises as trotting over poles and cantering in circles on either leg. Do not forget to teach the pony how to step back. He should also get used to being ridden out with other ponies, and, in particular, to going on a leading-rein being led by a rider on another, and much larger, pony.

At a rate of one half-hour lesson a day, all this should take about a month: a fortnight to get to 'backing' and a fortnight's schooling afterwards. That is a bare minimum, but even so it is a great deal more than most Shetlands receive, unfortunately.

BREAKING TO HARNESS

The training for a driving pony proceeds in a similar way in the early stages. But note the advice of Mrs Parsons, one of the most experienced Shetland pony whips: she says that *before* you lay out any money for harness or a vehicle, make sure that the pony is suitable, that is, that it is quiet in traffic and will never kick.[5] To test the pony's reaction to traffic, proceed as for a riding pony (*see* above). The kicking is more difficult, as it is hard to devise a test that is fair. You could stuff a paper sack with some straw and bump it against the pony's hocks while he is standing tied up and not expecting anything. If he does kick neither you nor he will get hurt.

Supposing that all has gone well, you will now require a set of harness. Breast harness is best for Shetlands for all purposes, and is

Fig 116 Breaking in a pony for driving: getting him used to wearing the harness. The guinea-pig in this series of photographs is Mrs Swinscow's Robin's Brae Irvine, who very patiently pretended to be a beginner when he is of course an old hand.

Fig 117 Going out for walks to meet traffic.

Fig 118   Long-reining wearing the full set of harness.

best for breaking in any horse. An exercise set made of nylon webbing is fine for this stage. Start with the bridle, which will have winkers (or blinkers); make sure these are set wide enough away from the pony's face, as it frightens a pony very much if his eyelashes brush against the inside of his winkers. Lead the pony around in the bridle at home until he has got used to it, then out on the roads again. The next stage is getting him used to wearing the rest of the harness. Put the pad on the first time, next the crupper, then the breast collar (improvise some way of securing the trace buckle to the tug to keep it in place without traces), then the breeching (tie the breeching strap to the tug). This will look like an awful lot of harness on a small pony but he must get used to it. Lead him round first, then begin long-reining.

This phase is rather different than it is for a riding pony, for the harness pony gets its forward aids from the driver's voice and whip, and these are available now. Make sure the pony knows his own name. You need a quiet place to practise, ideally a large yard, though a grass surface will do. Get the pony to walk, trot and stop at your command. You will find that it is quite strenuous running round

183

your yard behind your pony even if he is trotting quite slowly – for him. He must also learn to back (so few harness ponies do this properly). Do not, whatever you do, haul a pony back by the mouth. If you have someone to help you, get them to push him back by the chest while you call out 'Back'; if you are on your own, you will have to stand beside the pony, prompting it to go back by pushing its chest or arm while at the same time holding the reins, in one hand, just behind the pad.

Perhaps this is the moment to mention that it is perfectly possible to break a Shetland pony for harness single-handed, provided that you have a suitable safe yard in which to do the training. It is possible with Shetlands and not with bigger ponies simply because you can reach everything at once with a Shetland.

You must also teach your pony to stand still in his harness without being tied up. Start by facing him towards a wall or fence where there are no particular temptations in any directions, and gradually increase the length of time he is expected to stand there. Before you go on to the actual pulling part of the exercise, go back on to the roads with the pony in full harness and driven on long reins. Even though the pony was quite used to traffic when he had you by his side to reassure him, he may have some misgivings when on the road with you right away behind him. It is important to get him happy about this, because the next time you come out will be with you actually driving the vehicle.

Pulling is not difficult; ponies seem to do it naturally. Put the traces on, and lengthen them with extra straps or twine. If you have an assistant, get them to pull back on the traces while you drive the pony in long reins as normal; without an assistant you just have to do the pulling yourself with your right hand while you hold the long reins in your left. Similarly, you must teach the pony to put its weight into the breeching when going back. This is easiest with an assistant standing in front providing the pull on the breeching straps while you 'drive' but can also be done yourself standing beside the pony with reins in one hand and breeching straps (tied together with a piece of twine going round the pad terrets) in the other.

The pony's first actual load is something like a log or a bale of straw, attached to the end of the (extended) traces (use a quick-release knot). The pony will probably have no problem at all with the pulling but may find getting the load moving an odd feeling. At this stage add a bit of noise to the load to imitate the rattles and

184

Fig 119   Learning to pull.

Fig 120   Pulling a mock load.

Fig 121   Wearing sticks to get a feel of what the shafts will be
like.

squeaks of a vehicle; a bit of chain or a tin tied to the load and
dragging on the ground will do. Next let the pony have an idea of
what the shafts will feel like, by putting a cane through each of the
tugs and tied to the breeching. Walk him round in tight curves with
these so that he really does feel them (some ponies dislike this
feeling greatly at first).

Now you are ready to put-to for the first time. It is best to start
with an exercise cart, because it is light, quiet and easy for you to get
in and out of. Ideally you have an assistant, who brings the cart up
from behind and slips the shafts into the tugs while you are in
charge at the end of the reins. Do not do up the traces, just in case
you need to get the pony out in a hurry if he panics, but let the
assistant hold the shaft into the tug (on one side only will be
enough); the best thing is not to have the traces on at all but just to
secure the trace buckles to the tugs. Do not get into the vehicle yet,

Fig 122   Putting-to for the first time.

Fig 123   The driver gets in cautiously the first time . . .

Fig 124   . . . but is soon off on a tour of the farm.

Fig 125   A Shetland stallion is quiet enough for a child to ride:
Anna Staveley can easily manage Lakeland Lightning even
with a hound's leash in one hand. (Photo by Herbert Ballard.)

Fig 126 A team of ponies is put together for the first time,
and starts work in long reins. These are Mrs Adorian's ponies.

Fig 127 The same team is soon ready to drive away.

just drive from the ground, teaching the pony to turn the vehicle by pushing the end of the shaft with his shoulder. If you are on your own, stand beside the pony holding the shaft into the tug with your right hand and driving with your left (it is easier to use a pair of riding reins for this so that you do not have yards of spare rein trailing round your feet). When your pony is quite happy between the shafts you can do up the traces, but continue to drive him from the ground. Get him to trot now in straight lines and round corners, and to back. Put a load in the cart.

The final stage is to get into the cart and drive properly. If the cart is well balanced there should not be much weight on the pony's back. It is highly unlikely that it will be much perturbed at this stage after such a thorough training, but be sure to practise thoroughly round your yard or field before you take him out on the road. This is the time at which an assistant would be the most help, to be on hand if things should go wrong, but it is possible to do it on one's own. Shetland stallions are no trouble to break in, and they are perfectly reliable for both harness work and riding, even for children.

Fig 128   A pair as seen from the box seat: Mrs Handcock's
Apollo and Courtier of Woodbury.

Fig 129   A simple turnout: Mrs Braithwaite with Beacon Andrew.

Fig 130   A sophisticated turnout: the late Major Cox driving a
tandem.

PAIRS AND TEAMS

Ponies that know what to do in single harness should have no
trouble being driven in a pair or a team. The pole will feel a bit
different from the shafts, so try out the pair with some sort of
improvised pole before they are put to the vehicle. A tandem is
another matter: it is said to be the hardest type of driving of all. In
theory any two ponies that have been well schooled in long reins
and well broken to harness should have no problem, but it still takes
a lot of getting used to.[6]

15

Tailpiece

Let's drink a toast to Shetland ponies. But first, a nice little story concerning Shetlands and drink. The late-nineteenth century was

Fig 131 'Cheers!' from all ponies and people at the Swan Inn, Middleton, Lancs. (Photo by *Daily Mail*.)

the heyday of the temperance movement, and in many industrial cities and ports well-intentioned gentlefolk organised societies to help the poor rid themselves of the curse of drink. This happened in Lerwick, too, and indeed the number of reformers seems to have been uncommonly high for such a small town. Mr Robert Sinclair, one of the leading lights of the Lerwick Temperance Society, travelled widely on the Society's business:

> On one occasion he was in Edinburgh and went to a circus, the principal attraction of which was a Shetland pony, possessed, it was claimed, of more than ordinary equine intelligence, and which could answer questions in a most satisfactory manner. After performing one or two simple tricks, the pony was asked to point out the man who was very fond of a dram. Walking across to where our friend was sitting, the pony stopped before this bright and shining light of temperance, and gravely bowed its head, which, Sinclair afterwards complained to a friend, was particularly hard lines coming as it did from a fellow countryman.[1]

Assuming, then, that we all *are* fond of the dram, the toast is, 'The Shetland Ponies – God Bless Them!'

Notes

Introduction

1.   J.J.R. Meiklejohn, Introduction to *Shetland Pony Stud Book* (Shetland Pony Stud-Book Society, 1891), vol. 1.
2.   *Shetland in Statistics* (Shetland Islands Council Research and Development Department, 1987), p. 11.
3.   Sir Walter Scott, *The Pirate* (Constable, 1822), vol. 1, p. 257.
4.   C. and A. Douglas, *The Shetland Pony* (Blackwood, 1913), p. 109.
5.   Major Cox's words to Mrs Adorian, reported in her letter to the Shetland Pony Stud-Book Society Magazine 1983; his book is Maurice C. Cox, *The Shetland Pony* (A. & C. Black, 1965).
6.   C. and A. Douglas, *op. cit.*, p. 111.

Chapter 1

1.   George Gaylord Simpson, *Horses: the story of the horse family in the modern world* (Oxford University Press, 1951), p. 26.
2.   Richard Leakey, *The Making of Mankind* (Michael Joseph, 1981), pp. 193–6.
3.   Robert Brydon, Introduction to *Shetland Pony Stud Book*, vol. 1, p. xl.
4.   J. Cossar Ewart, 'The Making of the Shetland Pony', Appendix to *The Shetland Pony*, by C. and A. Douglas (Blackwood, 1913), p. 120.
5.   J.R.C. Hamilton, *Excavations at Jarlshof, Shetland* (Ministry of Works, Edinburgh, 1956).
6.   J.R. Allen, *Early Christian Monuments of Scotland* (Neill & Co., 1903), Fig. 4.
7.   Cox, *op. cit.*, pp. 40–3; C. and A. Douglas, *op. cit.*, pp. 5–12.
8.   Simpson, *op. cit.*, p. 26.
9.   *Orkneyinga Saga*, trans. J.A. Hjaltalin and G. Goudie (Edmonston & Douglas, 1873), pp. 150–1.
10. C. and A. Douglas, *op. cit.*, p. 46.
11. Cox, *op. cit.*, p. 41.
12. L. Edmonston, *New Statistical Account of Shetland 1841*, cited in Introduction to *Shetland Pony Stud Book*, vol. 1.
13. Cox, *op. cit.*, p. 40.
14. Quoted in Cox, *ibid.*, p. 40.
15. C. and A. Douglas, *op. cit.*, p. 11.
16. *Ibid.*, p. 6.
17. Cox, *op. cit.*, p. 40.

Chapter 2

1. John Smith, *A Description of the Islands of Shetland, &c., by Captain John Smith, who was employed there by the Earle of Pembrock in the year 1633, and stayed a whole Twelve Month there* (repr. Scottish History Society, 1908), p. 65.
2. Robert Monteith, *A Description of the Islands of Orkney and Zetland in the Year 1633* (repr. Thomas G. Stevenson, 1845), pp. 21–2.
3. Hugh Leigh, *A General Geographical Description of Zetland* (repr. Scottish History Society, 1908), p. 250.
4. John Brand, *A Brief Description of Orkney, Zetland, Pightland-Firth & Caithness* (George Mosman, 1701), pp. 77–9.
5. Mr Campbell, *An Exact and Authentic Account of the greatest White Herring Fishery in Scotland, carried on yearly in the Island of Zetland by the Dutch only,* repr. in *Tracts on Orkney and Shetland 1750–1801* (Library of Society of Antiquaries of Scotland), p. 8.
6. Cited in Cox, *op. cit.,* p. 18.
7. Christina Jamieson, in *Hjaltland Miscellany,* vol. 2 (Lerwick, 1937), p. xxi.
8. Sir Walter Scott, *op. cit.,* vol. 1, p. 258.
9. Samuel Hibbert (later Hibbert Ware), *A Description of the Shetland Islands* (Constable, 1822), p. 157.
10. Sir Walter Scott, *op. cit.,* vol. 1, pp. 256–7.
11. Harold Raeburn, *Journal for 1895* (unpubl.; Royal Scottish Museum), cited in L.S.V. and U.M. Venables, *Birds and Mammals of Shetland* (Oliver & Boyd, 1955), pp. 6–7.
12. Eliza Edmonston, *Sketches and Tales of the Shetland Islands* (Sutherland & Knox, 1856), pp. 50–6.
13. Cited in Cox, *op. cit.,* p. 29.
14. For accounts of the gear for flitting peats *see* Marie Brooker, 'Shetland Island Harness', *Shetland Pony Stud-Book Society Magazine* (1982), p. 40, and Cox, *op. cit.,* pp. 122–4 and Plate 4.
15. E.S. Reid Tait (ed.), *Hjaltland Miscellany,* vol. 4 (Lerwick, 1947), p. 35.
16. C. and A. Douglas, *op. cit.,* p. 44.
17. Thomas Gifford, *A Historical Description of the Zetland Islands in the Year 1733* (repr. Thomas G. Stevenson, 1879), pp. 22–3.
18. Eliza Edmonston, *op. cit.,* p. 51.

Chapter 3

1. C. and A. Douglas, *op. cit.,* pp. 104–5.
2. Eliza Edmonston, *op. cit.,* p. 52.
3. Cox, *op. cit.,* p. 27.
4. Tom Raikes, *Diary and Reminiscences of Social Life, from 1831 to 1847,* cited in S. Sidney, *The Book of the Horse,* 2nd edition eds. James Sinclair and W.C.A. Blew (Cassell, 1892), p. 454.
5. S. Sidney, *The Book of the Horse,* 2nd edition eds. James Sinclair and W.C.A. Blew (Cassell, 1892), p. 223.
6. Figures given in the Introduction to the *Shetland Pony Stud Book,* vol. 1.
7. Cox, *op. cit.,* p. 80.
8. Sir Walter Gilbey, *Ponies Past and Present* (Vinton, 1900), p. 82.
9. Sidney, *op. cit.,* p. 222.

10. Frank Townend Barton, *Ponies and All About Them* (John Long, 1911), p. 166.
11. Sidney, *op. cit.*, p. 224.
12. Sidney, *op. cit.*, p. 457.
13. Digby Collins, cited in Sidney, *op. cit.*, p. 424.
14. Cox, *op. cit.*, p. 31.
15. Gilbey, *op. cit.*, p. 83.
16. R.W.R. Mackenzie, 'The Shetland Pony', in Townend Barton, *op. cit.*, p. 217.
17. Roy Church, *The History of the British Coal Industry* (Clarendon Press, 1986), vol. 3, p. 196.
18. Church, *op. cit.*, p. 365.
19. Robert Brydon, 'Employment after leaving Shetland', in *Shetland Pony Stud Book*, vol. 1.
20. J. Benson, *British Coalminers in the Nineteenth Century: A Social History* (Gill & MacMillan, 1980), p. 80. Shocking though these figures are, they are in fact no worse than for many other occupations; agricultural labour was even more dangerous.

Chapter 4

1. Raeburn, *op. cit.*, p. 64.
2. Campbell, *op. cit.*, p. 8.
3. Highland Society of Scotland, *Observations on the Islands of Shetland* (1801), vol. 2, p. 7.
4. John and James Ingram, 'Unst', in *New Statistical Account of Shetland 1841* (Blackwood, 1845), p. 45.
5. That was the number estimated in 1822 (*see* Introduction to *Shetland Pony Stud Book*, vol. 1); there was no reason for it to have changed very much over the next 30 years.
6. Figures in an article in the *Shetland Advertiser* (1862), cited by Cox, *op. cit.*, p. 30.
7. 'The Druid' (H.H. Dixon), in *Field and Fern* (1865), cited in C. and A. Douglas, *op. cit.*
8. C. and A. Douglas, *op. cit.*, p. 27.
9. Cox, *op. cit.*, p. 32.
10. Brydon, *op. cit.*
11. 'The Druid', *op. cit.*
12. Official statistics cited in Introduction to *Shetland Pony Stud Book*, vol. 1.
13. For the Londonderry stud, *see* Cox, *op. cit.*, pp. 33 and 60–5, Gilbey, *op. cit.*, pp. 84–5, and Mackenzie, *op. cit.*, pp. 208–9.
14. See *Shetland Pony Stud Book*, vol. 1. The other Englishman was Lord Arthur Cecil of Tunbridge, a fanatical breeder of ponies of many different sorts.
15. Brydon, *op. cit.*, pp. xl–xli.
16. Mackenzie, *op. cit.*, p. 209.
17. C. and A. Douglas, *op. cit.*, p. 53.
18. *Ibid.*, pp. 70–1.
19. *Ibid.*, p. 55.
20. *Ibid.*, pp. 61–2.
21. *Ibid.*, p. 49.

Chapter 5

1. Figures for the sale are given in Cox, *op. cit.*, p. 66.
2. The conversion factor may be even higher than the × 50 I have used here, which is based on data from *Whitaker's Almanac 1989* (J. Whitaker, 1989), pp. 241 and 1059. Calculations on purchasing power are bedevilled by the fact that at different times people buy different things: there is no 1899 price for a microwave oven. I looked at something that Shetland breeders bought both then and now, i.e. registration for their ponies; in 1899 this was 2s 6d per entry and now it is £10, a factor of ×80 (*see Shetland Pony Stud Book*, vols. 9 and 88). That would make the average price of a pony at the Londonderry sale £1,680 and the top price over £10,000.
3. Mackenzie, *op. cit.*, p. 210.
4. *Shetland Pony Stud Book*, vols 2 and 12.
5. This interesting story is told in Cox, *op. cit.*, pp. 36–9. I am grateful to Mr Nicolson of Brindister, who kindly lent me the early volumes of the Shetland Islands Stud Book.
6. R.S. Summerhayes, *Elements of Riding* (Country Life, 1937), p. 86.
7. H. Faudel-Phillips, *Breaking and Schooling and other Horse Knowledge Practised and Proved*, 2nd edn (J.A. Allen, 1973), p. 102. This book was first published after the Second World War, but was written, as Major Faudel-Phillips explains in his Foreword, in the late 1920s.
8. Cox, *op. cit.*, p. 75.
9. Again the calculation is based on the comparative price of entering a pony in the Stud Book.
10. Cox, *op. cit.*, p. 85.
11. Glenda Spooner, in W.E. Lyon (ed.) *Youth in the Saddle* (Collins, 1955), p. 33.

Chapter 8

1. 'Wanderer', 'Ponies at work and play', *The Field*, 12 June 1920.
2. International Horse Show Catalogue 1920, cited in Maurice Cox, 'Shetland Ponies in Harness', *Shetland Pony Stud-Book Society Magazine* (1982), pp. 35–6.
3. S.C. Swannack, in *Shetland Pony Stud-Book Society Magazine* (Spring 1968), p. 26.
4. D.L.V. Morgan-Davies, 'Shetlands for Combined Driving', *Shetland Pony Stud-Book Society Magazine* (1982), p. 28.
5. E.H. Parsons, 'Driving and Riding Section Shetland Pony Driving Tour', *Shetland Pony Stud-Book Society Magazine* (Spring 1975), pp. 24–6.
6. Wendy Wright, 'Small draft horses for small holdings', *Shetland Pony Stud-Book Society Magazine* (1979), p. 47.

Chapter 11

1. Monteith, *op. cit.*, p. 24.
2. B. Myers, 'The Ponies of Shetland Heights', *Shetland Pony Stud-Book Society Magazine* (1980), pp. 45–6.
3. S.D. Elliott, *The Shetland Pony* (Boston, 1906), cited in Tom Ryder, 'The Shetland Pony', *Journal of the Carriage Association of America* (1986).

4.   Quoted in Mackenzie, *op. cit.*, p. 216.
5.   *Ibid.*
6.   Much of my data on the history of Shetlands in America is from Ryder, *op. cit.*
7.   L. Frank Bedell, *The Shetland Pony* (1960), cited in Cox, *op. cit.*, p. 34.
8.   George C. Saunders, *Your Horse*, 2nd edn (Van Nostrand, 1966), pp. 24–5.
9.   Antonio P. Fachiri, 'The Midget Horses of Arizona', *Riding* (Winter 1944), pp. 188–9.
10.   Jim Hill, 'Miniatures in the West', *American Shetland Pony Journal* (December 1975), p. 44.
11.   Lady Joan Gore-Langton, 'These ponies are miniature Shetlands', *Horse and Hound*, 15 January 1971.
12.   C. and A. Douglas, *op. cit.*, p. 109.
13.   This and other data following are from D.M. Patterson, 'Shetland Pony Exports 1890–1987', *Shetland Pony Stud-Book Society Magazine* (1988), p. 27.

Chapter 12

1.   Eliza Edmonston, *op. cit.*, p. 52.
2.   In the case of colts registered below four years old, I have added an allowance as follows: two-year-olds 2in, unless they are under 33in at two in which case 1½in, three-year-olds 1in unless they are under 34in at three in which case ¾in. If a pony's height is not an exact number of inches it has been counted as the next number up, i.e. 35½in counts as 36in.
3.   August Weismann, *Studies in the Theory of Descent*, translated by R. Meldola from *Studien zur Descendenztheorie*, 2 vols., 1875–6, with an introduction by Charles Darwin (Samson Low, 1882), pp. 634–44. Weismann's most simple experiment to prove that acquired characteristics cannot be inherited consisted of cutting the tails off mice. The resulting offspring did, of course, have tails even though their parents did not: the tail was 'there' in the genetics even if the actual tail had been cut off.
4.   The original research is in Konrad Lorenz, *Studies in Animal and Human Behaviour*, vol. 2 (Methuen, 1971), but there is also an excellent and amusing summary in Stephen Jay Gould, *The Panda's Thumb* (Norton, 1980), pp. 95–107, also reprinted by Pelican Books.
5.   It is interesting that in the Douglases' day the under-34in ponies do seem to have been of the dwarf type, unsound because of disproportionately short legs. This type is extremely unusual now. The Douglases do not appear to have seen the neotenous type of miniature; perhaps it is a recent arrival in the Shetland's genetic repertoire. *See* C. and A. Douglas, *op. cit.*, pp. 67–8.
6.   C. and A. Douglas, *op. cit.*, p. 68.

Chapter 13

1.   The address of the Shetland Pony Stud-Book Society is Pedigree House, 6 King's Place, Perth PH2 8AD. Tel. 0738 23471. The magazine comes out every spring.
2.   Prices at the auction sales held each autumn at Baltasound, Lerwick, Aberdeen and Reading are reported in the following year's *Shetland Pony Stud-Book Society Magazine*.
3.   Spooner, *op. cit.*, p. 33.

Chapter 14

1. C. and A. Douglas, *op. cit.*, p. 86.
2. Cox, *op. cit.*, p. 141.
3. Eliza Edmonston, *op. cit.*, pp. 54–5.
4. C. and A. Douglas, *op. cit.*, pp. 94–5.
5. E.H. Parsons, 'Driving Shetland Ponies', *Shetland Pony Stud-Book Magazine* (1987), pp. 10–13.
6. An excellent book is Janet Holyoake, *Learning to Drive Ponies* (Faber & Faber, 1948) in which the guinea-pig tandem is a pair of Shetlands – driven in open bridles (i.e. without winkers) to make things more difficult.

Chapter 15

1. E.S. Reid Tait (ed.), *The Hjaltland Miscellany* (Lerwick, 1934), vol. 1, p. 51.

Bibliography

Allen, J.R., *Early Christian Monuments of Scotland* (Neill & Co., 1903)

Bedell, L. Frank, *The Shetland Pony* (1960), cited in M.C. Cox, *The Shetland Pony* (A. & C. Black, 1965), p. 34

Benson, J. *British Coalminers in the Nineteenth Century: A Social History* (Gill & MacMillan, 1980)

Brand, J., *A Brief Description of Orkney, Zetland, Pightland-Firth & Caithness* (George Mosman, 1701)

Brooker, M., 'Shetland Island Harness' *Shetland Pony Stud-Book Society Magazine* (1982), p. 40

Brydon, R., 'Introduction' to *Shetland Pony Stud Book* (Shetland Pony Stud-Book Society, 1891), Vol. 1

Campbell, J., *An Exact and Authentic Account of the greatest White Herring Fishery in Scotland carried out yearly in the Island of Zetland by the Dutch only*, repr. from 1750 edn. (William Brown, Edinburgh, 1885)

Church, R., *The History of the British Coal Industry* (Clarendon Press, 1986)

Cossar Ewart, J., 'The Making of the Shetland Pony', Appendix to C. and A. Douglas, *The Shetland Pony* (Blackwood, 1913)

Cox, Maurice C., 'Shetland Ponies in Harness' *Shetland Pony Stud-Book Society Magazine* (1982), pp. 35–6

The Shetland Pony (A. & C. Black, 1965)

Dixon, H.H., ('The Druid') *Field and Fern* (1865)

Douglas, C. and A., *The Shetland Pony* (Blackwood, 1913)

Edmonston, Eliza, *Sketches and Tales of the Shetland Islands* (Sutherland & Knox, 1856)

Edmonston, L., *New Statistical Account of Shetland 1841* (Blackwood, 1845)

Elliott, S.D., *The Shetland Pony* (Boston, 1906)

Fachiri, Antonio P., 'The Midget Horses of Arizona' *Riding* (Winter, 1944), pp. 188–9

Faudel-Phillips, H., *Breaking and Schooling and other Horse Knowledge Practised and Proved*, 2nd edn (J.A. Allen, 1973)

Gifford, T., *A Historical Description of the Zetland Islands in the year 1733* (repr. Thomas G. Stevenson, 1879)

Gilbey, Sir Walter, *Ponies Past and Present* (Vinton, 1900)

Gore-Langton, Lady Joan, 'These ponies are miniature Shetlands' *Horse and Hound* (15 January, 1971)

Gould, Stephen Jay, *The Panda's Thumb* (Norton, 1980)

Hamilton, J.R.C., *Excavations of Jarlshof, Shetland* (Ministry of Works Edinburgh, 1956)

Hibbert, S., *A Description of the Shetland Islands* (Constable, 1822)

Highland Society of Scotland, *Observations on the Islands of Shetland* (1801)

Hill, J., 'Miniatures in the West' *American Shetland Pony Journal* (December, 1975), p. 44

Hjaltalin, J.A. and Goudie, G., (transl.) *Orkneyinga Saga* (Edmonston & Douglas, 1873)

Holyoake, Janet, *Learning to Drive Ponies* (Faber & Faber, 1948)

Ingram, J. and J., 'Unst', in *New Statistical Acount of Shetland 1841* (Blackwood, 1845), p. 45.

Jamieson, Christina (ed.), *Hjaltland Miscellany*, Vol. 2 (Lerwick, 1937)

Leakey, R., *The Making of Mankind* (Michael Joseph, 1981)

Leigh, H., *A General Geographical Description of Zetland* (repr. Scottish History Society, 1908)

Lorenz, Konrad, *Studies in Animal and Human Behaviour*, Vol. 2 (Methuen, 1971)

Lyon, W.E. (ed.) *Youth in the Saddle* (Collins, 1955)

Mackenzie, R.W.R., 'The Shetland Pony', in Townend Barton, F., *Ponies and All About Them* (John Long, 1911), pp. 205–30

Mayr, Ernst, *Evolution and the Diversity of Life* (Belknap, 1976)

Meiklejohn, J.J.R., Introduction to *Shetland Pony Stud Book* (Shetland Pony Stud-Book Society, 1891), Vol. 1

Monteith, R., *A Description of the Islands of Orkney and Zetland in the year 1633* (repr. Thomas G. Stevenson, 1845)

Morgan-Davies, D.L.V., 'Shetlands for Combined Driving' *Shetland Pony Stud-Book Society Magazine* (1982), pp. 28–9

Myers, B., 'The Ponies of Shetland Heights' *Shetland Pony Stud-Book Society Magazine* (1980), pp. 45–6

Parsons, E.H., 'Driving and Riding Section Shetland Pony Driving Tour' *Shetland Pony Stud-Book Society Magazine* (Spring, 1975), pp. 24–6

'Driving Shetland Ponies' *Shetland Pony Stud-Book Society Magazine* (1987), pp. 10–13

Patterson, D.M., 'Shetland Pony Exports 1890–1987' *Shetland Pony Stud-Book Society Magazine* (1988), p. 27

Raeburn, H., *Journal for 1895* (unpubl., Royal Scottish Museum), cited in Venables, L.S.V. and U.M., *Birds and Mammals of Shetland* (Oliver & Boyd, 1955)

Raikes, T., *Diary and Reminiscences of Social Life, from 1831 to 1847*, cited in Sidney , S., *The Book of Horse*, 2nd edn. (Cassell, 1892)

Reid Tait, E.S. (ed.), *Hjaltland Miscellany*, Vol. 1 (Lerwick, 1934) *Hjaltland Miscellany*, Vol. 4 (Lerwick, 1947)

Ryder, T., 'The Shetland Pony' *Journal of the Carriage Association of America* (1986)

Saunders, George C., *Your Horse*, 2nd edn (Van Nostrand, 1966)

Scott, Sir Walter, *The Pirate* (Constable, 1822)

Shetland Advertiser (1862)

Shetland in Statistics (Shetland Islands Council Research and Development Department, 1987)

Sidney, S., *The Book of the Horse*, 2nd edn (Cassell, 1892)

Simpson, G.G., *Horses: the story of the horse family* (Oxford University Press, 1951)

Smith, J., *A Description of the Islands of Shetland, &c, by Captain John Smith, who was employed there by the Earle of Pembrock in the year 1633, and stayed a whole Twelve Month there* (repr. Scottish History Society, 1908)

Spooner, Glenda, in Lyon, W.C., *Youth in the Saddle* (Collins, 1955), p. 33

Swannack, S.C., in *Shetland Pony Stud-Book Society Magazine* (Spring, 1968), p. 26

Townend Barton, F., *Ponies and All About Them* (John Long, 1911)

Venables, L.S.V. and U.M., *Birds and Mammals of Shetland* (Oliver & Boyd, 1955)

'Wanderer', 'Ponies at work and play' *The Field* (12 June, 1920)

Weismann, August, *Studies in the Theory of Descent*, transl. R. Meldola w. foreword by Charles Darwin, 2 vols (Sampson Low, 1882)

Whitaker's Almanac 1989 (J. Whitaker, 1988)

Wright, Wendy, 'Small draft horses for small holdings' *Shetland Pony Stud-Book Society Magazine* (1979), p. 47

Index

Italic numerals denote page numbers of illustrations

204